Indian Thought Between
Tradition
and the
Culture of Technology

Indian Thought Between
Tradition
and the
Culture of Technology

D. L. Johnson

D.K. Printworld (P) Ltd.
NEW DELHI-110015

Cataloging in Publication Data — DK

Johnson, D. L. (David Lawrence), 1941 -
   Indian thought between tradition and the
culture of technology.
   Includes bibliographical references (p.   ).
   Includes index.

    1. Technology — Social aspects — India.
    2. Technology and social change — India.
    I. Title.

ISBN 81-246-0046-5

First Published in India in 1995
© Author,1994

Published by :
D.K. Printworld (P) Ltd.
Regd. office : H-12, Bali Nagar
New Delhi - 110015
Phones : (011) 546-5926, 546-6019; *Fax* : (011) 546-5927

Typeset at : Shilpkar, New Delhi

Whether or not it draws on new scientific research, technology is a branch of moral philosophy, not of science.

— Paul Goodman

Contents

Preface

THIS book asserts that technology has become not only a measure of what it means to be civilized, it has created a culture of its own against which every traditional culture is forced to measure itself. In short, it is not art, literature or philosophy that measure human achievement today. Neither is it political or social structures that are the measure of human achievement. The new measure is technology.

How this new measure might have come to dominate modern societies is an historical question. Michael Adas' book titled *Machines as the Measure of Men* (1989) traces the adoption of technology as a measure through a study of imperialist ventures into Africa, India and China. Adas argues that the measure was promoted both by commerce and religion.

What such a measure might mean to a society still concerned about tradition is the subject of this book. India's encounter with a new constellation of compelling ideas and values that comprise modern technology occurred during the time India was dominated by Europeans, especially Great Britain. But a study of India is complicated by the fact that intellectuals of India confronted the developing culture of technology at the same time as they confronted imperialism. Thus two demands for a new way of life went together (the one imposed foreign rule, the other imposed a new measure of cultural achievement). The new political order, indeed, was buttressed by superior weaponry, industry, and techniques. But Westerners brought with them also the cultural ideals which provided the foundation for their technical superiority, ideals that soon became spelled out as ideals of objectivity, measurement, efficiency, and standardization. In short, from today's perspective, the significant culture that the British brought to India (however ignorant of it many of purveyors might have been) was the culture of technology.

It was, of course, the technology of weaponry, industry, and commerce that allowed Westerners to conquer and govern South Asia. But the ideas that shaped, and, indeed, drove modern technology did pose a threat to India's prized traditions (as, indeed, those ideas might be seen to pose a threat to every tradition). It remains to be seen whether it is, in fact, technology that stands as the major threat to Indians of both Hindu and Muslim persuasion. Such a statement is to suggest that it is not religious ideology or values so much as it is the intrusion of technology upon those values which divides Indians. The culture of technology irritates both sides equally. The irritant might be difficult to identify, however, since as Chapter 1 of this book argues, the culture of technology does not directly counter traditional ideas. Instead technology renders traditional ideas and values irrelevant; or it suggests that they ought to be put to different uses than they have been put to in the past.

In the pages that follow the sort of changes which technology requires of traditional ideas and values will be spelled out. This book poses the problem; and it discusses solutions generated by major thinkers of modern India. It will become clear that some Indian thinkers managed to deal with foresight — indeed, incredible insight — with the problems which modern technology poses for all contemporary societies. Yet this book stands as a beginning for further discussion.

I am aware that my central assertion that technology has become a new measure of cultural achievement is controversial. The charge of 'reductionism' might follow from a claim that technology is a determinant for societies today. I must assume as well that some readers might stand suitably armed to insist that a study of this sort is an instance of faulty reasoning, such as one might find to be *post hoc ergo propter hoc* ("after this, therefore because of this"). Neither is a legitimate charge. And what follows in this book I am prepared to defend as **material** truth, whatever the errors of **logical** truth some of the thinkers discussed might have committed in their writing.

Yet another issue which, no doubt, requires clarification is the issue of just what is meant by the word 'culture' in the phrase "the culture of technology". It is customary to think of culture as that body of arts devoted to representation and description, and which normally stands quite isolated from economic, social and political concerns of a society. Moreover, culture is ordinarily thought to be an elevating element within a society, an element which holds before people what is thought to be the best that has been created and known to a people. And, of course, culture is also thought to be something that provides a sense of identity for a people (for example, a person is provided an identity when conforming to ideals of texts such as *Bhagavad-Gita* or *Ramayana*).

But how might technology be thought of as a culture? In what sense might technology be isolated from economic, political, and social concerns of societies? Can it be thought of as something which is aesthetically elevating for people? And does technology (can technology) provide for people a sense of human identity?

Chapter 1 examines this issue, and there it is argued that technology has become in our time more than tools and skills: it is instead a constellation of ideas and values which require allegiance as a condition for both survival and progress in the contemporary world. The definition is crucial, I think. A person chooses a tool; but today no person chooses the values of technology any more than they choose a native language. In short, I am arguing that culture is a pattern of values, attitudes, and beliefs, and that the values, attitudes, and beliefs which promote technology are coming to dominate all societies. Chapter 2 considers the way in which India was introduced to the culture of technology. And Chapters 3, 4, and 5 are analyses of the ways in which major Indian thinkers of the twentieth century addressed the problem of technology as an alien culture imposed upon it by foreign rulers. And finally I wish to make some concluding remarks about technology, culture, and tradition.

It is, I think, important for Indian readers to keep in mind that India need not become like the United States of America in order to take advantage of what modern technology might provide. Americans surely have not solved the problem of how to hold to values of a tradition and at the same time to embrace the culture of technology. Yet, I think, there remain many Indian professionals who are inclined to scrap Indian tradition and to adopt the culture of technology because they have been encouraged to confuse prosperity with progress, consumption with culture, and wealth with wisdom. It is an unfortunate confusion; and much about life in the United States stands as demonstration of that confusion.

Yet, I do think that an exploration of what wise and perceptive Indians of the last one hundred years thought and wrote about modern technology and its perceived threat to tradition might assist us all in coping with that culture of technology with which we must live today. And it might be the case that India, with its strong commitments to tradition, might be able to solve the problems posed by the culture of technology.

Assistance in writing this book has come from many people. I am indebted to my faculty colleagues of the Department of Humanities at Indiana State University for their important encouragement. Also I owe much to Ms. Amy Springgs, who for a summer and much of a semester searched for, read and summarized with considerable skill a great body of books and journals. Her work captured time for me. And Ms. Lily Pong, working in a second language, mastered the technology to put into proper form for publication words that I poked out on a machine now thought to be quite obsolete.

During the time I worked on this manuscript, my dear wife, Rebecca, died. I miss her terribly — her kindness, her affection, indeed, her companionship. Yet a book lives, and there is much of her that continues with this book, not the least being an optimism about India.

D. L. Johnson

1

The Culture of Technology

TECHNOLOGY and culture are today congruent in much of the so-called **developed** world, and it seems that many people in the **developing** world seem convinced that to achieve such a congruence would gain for them the distinction of being **developed**. In short, in the minds of many people, it is a fact that there is a close relationship between technology and what is modern about modern culture. Moreover, to exhibit that closeness is a sign of development. Thus, how to bring the two closer together so that there might be no question of a conflict (in fact, that there might be a unity) is an intellectual preoccupation of many thinkers in the so-called developing world.

Yet it might be argued convincingly that technology and culture have always been connected through complicated interdependencies and interactions. The difference today, however, is that it is technology (along with the values which drive technological innovation and development) that exemplifies not only progress, but sophistication, even refinement.

A proper relationship of technology to a culture is a matter of long debate. Some trace the controversy back as far as the Greek thinkers of the classical era. Some Greeks thought technological change to mark intellectual development in the history of the human race. Technical skills were a mark of cultural advancement, it was said. And those people with a capacity to build tools and machines are to be admired. But other Greek thinkers (such as Plato) made a contrast between technology and intellect (the human mind ought to move beyond the applied arts to the fine arts, he maintained).

Colleges and universities in the Western world have tended to adopt the Platonist view of technology. The ancient distinction has continued by institutionalizing categories such as 'fine arts' over against 'applied arts', 'liberal studies' over against 'professional studies', and the 'studio arts' over against 'industrial arts'.

But now there are reasons to suspect that the Platonists have held a short-sighted view. Everyone must admit that new tools create opportunities for people to do things in new ways, to achieve new goals, and to re-organize their ways of living. It is a fact, for example, that an automobile both replaces a horse-drawn carriage and gets a person to a destination in considerably less time. But, in order to take advantage of a new opportunity provided by a new technology, people find themselves needing to live differently. Streets and roads require pavement, roadway signs, and legislation for proper driving; and all of these require industries to produce what will keep all of it going and working with some efficiency.

Technology, therefore, is a force that brings change. To know what it is about technology that brings such comprehensive change would seem to be a requirement for history, art, philosophy, and, indeed, literature (since, for example, a literature mass-produced for a mass market is likely to differ from a literature produced for a limited, exclusive readership). Today it is the case that technology is the major agent of change throughout the world. In fact, technology is so closely linked to culture that it seems to be creating its own new culture.

What is it that marks the changes brought by new technologies in our time? And how is it that these changes can be termed cultural changes?

The first indications of cultural change brought by technology seem to register as a social strain when a new technology is introduced to a society. The first indication of strain occurs when old ways of living (the older cultural values) and a new technology seem to be at variance with one another (some new techniques call into question or contradict old ways, as when the automobile makes the buggy whip an obsolete item or when washing machines replace people who formerly made a living washing other people's clothes). The strain appears to be simply a matter of social dislocation and/or unemployment.

But a second level of strain soon occurs between groups of people, some of whom prefer the old ways (the old culture). Yet a third level of strain occurs when pressure is felt to make distinct choices about whether the changes being made are right or wrong, good or bad. And sometimes decisions about good and bad, right and wrong, are not simply aesthetic decisions, but ethical decisions. Modern medical technology, for example, is directed toward extending indefinitely the lives of people. Such an effort forces a change in traditional cultural norms concerning the significance of both life and death. But the effort to extend life indefinitely poses ethical questions concerning how long and under what conditions life ought to be extended indefinitely.

Thus technology forces people to change many things: their habits of thought, their values, and even their goals for life and their anticipation of a meaningful death. Gradually a new culture emerges which generates new and different ideas concerning what sort of a life is the best life to live. What modern technology brings is the culture of technology.

Technology in Social and Cultural Change: The Steam Engine, the Factory, and Work

The relationship between technology and the life of a culture is apparent from a look at what happened to ordinary people and some traditional values when the factory system of production became widespread in America. During Jefferson's presidency at the beginning of the nineteenth century, American society was one in which most work was farm work or the work done by skilled craftsmen. Cities were fairly small compared to the cities of today, large factories were unknown, and a sense of individualism was fostered by the prevailing political philosophy as well as by the fact that a worker's efforts brought tangible rewards. Skill, commitment to hard work, tangible reward, and a sense of worth were tightly connected. And a cultural blueprint for respectability and success was clear to people — a blueprint that showed that a fulfilling life is one of individual effort that will bring its proper rewards.

But when technologists succeeded in applying steam machine power to the factory system of production, great changes took place. The factory system put machines and workers together to mass produce goods for which there came to be increasing demands by people who admired modern production techniques. To keep up with consumer demands, industrialists encouraged

people to leave the countryside for the promise of a
regular income through factory employment in the cities.
Eventually, an industrial empire many times more
productive than older, simpler systems of craft production
appeared.

Yet the new system of production brought by new
technology challenged many of the values that had been
central to the Jeffersonian era. The older meaning of
what it meant to be a productive member of a society did
not easily correspond to factory workers' employment
situations. An ordinary factory worker was neither a
craftsman nor an independent producer of goods; a
worker was in a sense owned by the person who owned
the factory (in a new and fundamental way, no factory
worker could see himself as an independent person).
Neither could a worker easily identify his interests or
concerns with the interests and concerns of the factory
owner, or even with the products passing along an
assembly line. A new work situation produced individual
and social strain. And older ideas and values about what
it meant to live well did not correspond to the new
situation.

The social strain produced by the factory system
eventually developed into collective behaviour and group
action that violently challenged both the new system
and the older values of work, respectability, and social
order. It is important to remember that both the new
system **and** the old values were challenged and forced to
change. Technology created its own culture with new
values and new goals for individuals to pursue in order
to acquire a sense of worth.

What occurred was a new definition of what it meant
to work, what it meant to achieve respectability, indeed,
what it meant to live a satisfying and fulfilled life. The

new factory system of production based on machine technology emptied or destroyed some old values at the same time as it created some new ones. Over a period of time new norms of proper behaviour emerged so that individual workers could again know what social and cultural expectations existed and what might be an appropriate life to live.

The introduction of the steam engine into the work life of Americans dramatically altered American culture. Some people (what might be thought of as an old cultural 'elite') continued to espouse the values of a pre-industrial society — the values of free enterprise, individualism, and the rewards of personal commitment and industry. And the old cultural elite continued to adhere to the old values of a pre-industrial society — the values of free enterprise, individualism, and the rewards of personal commitment and traditional culture — the culture holding high the ideals generated by reading the works of thinkers of the ancient world of Greece, Rome, as well as the works of the Christian and Jewish Fathers. But for most of the people who worked in the factories and mines, those values were now empty of any relevance to their lives as workers. A different culture began to emerge. New tools produced problems and tensions that eventually called for a new definition of work as well as for a new definition of what it meant to be a complete human being. In the process, of course, all social institutions such as family, politics, education, and religion were modified by the new culture. An elite might hold to tradition; but the realities of the new industrial order forced workers **and** managers to conform to new realities of the work place.

The Question of Technological Determinism

The realization that technology is firmly connected to

culture and, indeed, creates its own culture has led a number of influential thinkers of the twentieth century to claim that in our time it is technology that determines culture. The names Jacques Ellul, Lewis Mumford, Marshall McLuhan, Hannah Arendt, Herbert Marcuse, Pierre Teilhard de Chardin and Langdon Winner are associated with this view that technology of our time completely shapes and re-shapes human life according to its own dictates.

The Technological Determinist argument is that technology is not to be identified simply with tools that help people to do new things in new ways. The Determinist argument is that today's technology creates both a cultural style and a way of thinking which advocate a worldview. This worldview has come to dominate every so-called 'modern' society. The worldview and the way of living it advocates (indeed, demands) carries its own assumptions and dictates about what is important for people to achieve and to acquire, and it forces a way of living that demands a new morality, new procedures, and new goals for life. In a very real sense, technology as a culture is 'autonomous'.[1] And as such it is a culture that stands apart from people, it informs them of what is the best life to live, and it forces them to make significant adjustments about their views concerning what is an important and fulfilling life.

The 'Hard' Determinist Argument

The hard determinist argument concerning the culture of technology is rigorously argued by the French sociologist Jacques Ellul. Ellul claims that the fundamental values that drive 'autonomous' technology are **Rationality, Efficiency, Organization**, and **Standardization. Rationality** is the conviction that all

problems facing human beings can be resolved through
rational analyses and solutions derived through such
analyses. Technology advocates the practical application
of reason as the measure to be adopted for successful
living everywhere and at every level of social activity.
Emotions are to be suppressed and repressed, particularly when issues of how people ought to live arise.

The value of **Efficiency** serves as the ruling factor
when people must decide between two or more alternative
rational courses of action (confronted with the rational
alternatives of walking, riding a bicycle, or driving an
automobile to work, **Efficiency** will generally direct a
person to drive the automobile). Technology constantly
works to improve efficiency at every level of life.

Organization is a further extension of the rational
and efficient approach to living. In order to live by the
principles of rationality and efficiency, people must
organize themselves and their world in such a way that
actions of individuals and groups do not conflict, but fit
together in an orderly manner (for people to drive
automobiles, organization must occur that will arrange
for the rational and efficient production of automobiles,
the processing and distribution of fuel for them, the
uniform construction of streets and roads, the installation
of traffic signals, regulations for ownership and driving
automobiles, and the repair and maintenance equipment
necessary to keep all such things working properly). The
culture of technology forces **everything** to conform to
requirements for rationality, efficiency and organization.

Standardization follows from the demand for rational,
efficient, organized procedures. Standardization builds
upon organization to solve in advance all problems
which might frustrate the rational and efficient function
of the whole organization of technological devices (in

this case, from automobile design to traffic control to repair to maintenance to parking lots and parking garages). If all aspects of life can be standardized, then efficiency and organization are unhindered.

Once the worldview of technology is adopted, all other options are dismissed by people as 'irrational', 'inefficient', 'disorganized', or 'inconsistent'. As a consequence, human life is put under the rule of **Determinative Technology**.

A symbol of capitulation to determinative technology is the mechanical clock. With the widespread use of the mechanical clock to measure time, human experiences which might have been determined by seasonal rhythms, biology, personal inclination, or whim are repressed, ignored, or even forgotten. The clock, worn on the wrist or hung on the wall, re-shapes life according to its demands, its requirements. And anyone living in a society that uses the clock is expected to organize and to standardize life in terms of the clock. To be late for school, for work, or for dinner because of individual preferences, desires, or needs is to violate standards dictated by a tool. And whoever appears late receives the regular and persistent censure of people living in any society dominated by Technological Determinism.[2]

The 'Soft' Determinist Argument

Not every Determinist thinker is convinced that human choices concerning technology have been eliminated; nor does every Determinist thinker conclude that the culture of technology is altogether bad. Some thinkers, convinced that there is a higher power that oversees and, indeed, determines the fate of the earth and of humanity, put a positive interpretation upon the determining power of technology. Among these thinkers

were the Christian priest and paleontologist Pierre
Teilhard de Chardin and the Indian philosopher
Aurobindo Ghose. Technology does determine how
people live, they insisted, but it is working for the
betterment of all humanity. For them, technology as a
culture — a way of thinking and a method of material
improvement — is part of a divine plan for the world.

Teilhard in his scientific and religious writings
thought of technology as a stage of human development
that follows upon a long process of evolution. The
material 'stuff' of the universe has been developing over
millennia into increasingly more elaborate organizations.
This evolutionary process Teilhard called **complexification**. Subatomic particles change into atoms, atoms
change into inorganic molecules, inorganic molecules
change into organic molecules, and so on until living
cells and multicellular units appear. Complexification
is the tendency of each new development to integrate
with a previous level, to elaborate on it, and to build
upon it. Human life and society are simply one stage of
the development that began with subatomic units. Since
the process began prior to the appearance of human life,
there is no reason to believe that the evolutionary
process will stop with human life as it is known today.

Yet a new mode of evolution did occur with the
appearance of the human race. Human life brought the
noosphere — a level of self-consciousness, self-
awareness, and reflective thinking. Prior to the noosphere, evolution occurred in a mechanical fashion
through the built-in tendency of energy to link similar
elements together and to produce through such union
greater complexity and concentricity. The noosphere,
however, allows energy to manifest itself in mental
processes that can guide, re-direct, and change the
stream of evolution.

The human mind with its capacity for rational analysis is a continuation of the evolutionary process. But because human life is limited to the earth, complexification becomes a complexification of rational analysis and rational productivity. Yet the whole process is integral: material stuff is incorporated into mental activity. Ideas that integrate reason with matter emerge to encounter earlier integrations of matter and mind. And such a complexification continues toward a state of intense unification of psychic energy and social organization. Finally a condition Teilhard termed 'omega point' will be reached by the human race.[3]

Technology as thinking and doing, then, is part of the universal evolutionary process. There is no way to stop technological change, and there is no good reason to want to stop it. And, to Teilhard, the technological society promises to save humanity from its biological limitations, its tendencies toward irrationality, and from base inclinations toward disorganization. Technology promises a new society distinct from precious societies. But the new life brings changes: it "shows signs ... of requiring us ... to sacrifice our individuality". In other words, the values of individualism, autonomy, freedom, and personal responsibility that evolved out of particular social conditions are not the end or high point of evolution. Such values are but a step along the way.

Evolving technology forces a higher mode of thought that requires giving up values of previous eras. Technology may force "totalization of political regimes", closer physical relations among people, and "the increasing impossibility of being or acting or thinking **alone**. ..." Technology might even eliminate eventually the sense of a personal, free, independent self. Yet people need not fear such developments: it is part of a divine plan.

The New Tribalism of a Technological Culture

Many thinkers in the humanities are not at all inclined toward the conviction (belief) that there is a divine purpose to what is occurring with the culture of technology. Yet these people share the assumption that technology today dominates, directs, and controls human life. One of the most creative and controversial recent thinkers was Marshall McLuhan, who maintained that the dominant technologies of a society (those technologies which attract the attention of most people) always end up re-making people.

McLuhan admitted that the dominant technologies at one time in Western culture did encourage values of rationality, efficiency, organization and standardization. But not so any longer, he insisted. The emergence of the electronic era brought a new and different set of cultural values to determine life. Television, computers, communication satellites, and lasers do not **push** people toward something new; instead, these technologies **pull** people toward something new. The dominant technologies today do not drive people so much as they entice people. But people are being re-made, nevertheless.

In his books *The Gutenberg Galaxy and Understanding Media: The Extensions of Man*, McLuhan identified himself with technological determinist views. But major technologies today, he insisted, are **media** technologies, those tools are used to mediate between people and their environments.

According to McLuhan, all technologies extend some function of the human body so that a person might relate easily or successfully to an environment. Technologies in this sense are tools. But the technologies people use are actually tools that extend them in some manner. An automobile is a tool that serves to extend a person's legs, and it mediates between a person and a spatial environment which needs to be traversed. A person might walk or run to travel a distance; but the medium of an automobile covers the space in less time and with less physical effort. The technology allows a person to deal easily and successfully with an environment at the same time as it extends the person's legs. Ordinary people find themselves enticed toward using a tool such as an automobile.

Yet at the same time as a technology extends some function, it also eliminates some function. When a person uses the medium of an automobile, that person's legs become irrelevant, they are eliminated from any significant role in the activity of movement in a particular environment. The automobile does what needs to be done and the bodily equipment is replaced by the medium. Clothes, too, in this sense are technologies: they function as an extension of the skin of someone who wears them. But when someone wears clothes, **the clothes** relate the environment, not the person's skin.

Modern technologies extend considerably the capacities of people both relate to and even to control environments of all sorts. But at the same time as extensions of some capacities occur, some capacities are reduced and eliminated. This means that by creating new tools, people keep remaking themselves by extending parts of themselves and by eliminating parts of themselves. Electronic technologies of television, the telephone, the computer, and the satellite extend significantly the capacity of people to communicate. But a reduction and an elimination occur at the same time as an extension takes place.

McLuhan maintained that the significant change taking place with communication technologies is a biological change — a change in the balance of the sense-organs. Seeing, hearing, tasting, touching, and smelling are all extended by electronic technologies. But because communication occurs primarily by seeing and hearing, it is the extension of these capacities by electronic means that is significant. Yet to extend one capacity is to overload it in such a way that other senses are reduced. Attention cannot be given to other sense-organs because one or two are overloaded. The result is an imbalance of the sensory capacities, indeed, the sensory organs.

But sensory imbalance is not new. A close look at the past suggests that a skewing of balance for the sense-organs occurred once before in the history of cultures. A dramatic change in sensory balance took place with the development of the printing press in the fifteenth century. Before that time, the dominant sense was the sense of hearing. People got their information, their news, their understanding of the world, by hearing from others about what was taking place in the world. Such a sensory orientation created a certain type of human being. The 'hearing' person was **Tribal man** — the human being that lived spontaneously, unreflectively, emotionally. Tribal man had no accurate sense of time (there were no clocks to turn time into space, something to be seen and measured); stories that were told by these people of the ancient world (and which were eventually written down and preserved as 'epic' poems such as *The Odyssey, The Iliad* and *The Mahabharata*) convey this absence of a sense of historical time. People who did not read or write and who got all of their news through hearing possessed little or no sense of history in the modern sense of the term because there were no reference books for anyone to consult. Words could not be easily preserved, examined, or analyzed. Words were part of a hearing experience; sometimes words were remembered. But everything important happened in the immediate present (even to tell a story of a past event transformed that event into the present).

Great change took place when writing transferred sound into sight (hearing into seeing). Turning sound into sight also turned words into things that could be localized, preserved, contained, and analyzed. Writing brought its own imbalance to the sense-organs, and sight began to replace sound, seeing replaced hearing, for those who could read and write.

The invention of the printing press as a tool that could produce great quantities of written items quickly, items that ranged from books to newspapers, intensified the orientation toward seeing. In short, the new technology imposed its own changes. Many more people could get their information by seeing it rather than by hearing it. The widespread conversion of sound into sight through the medium of the printing press encouraged people to take the time to look carefully at words, to arrange them carefully, and to give attention to style in writing and printing. For many people, language became intimately associated with writing rather than with speaking or hearing.

Print technology created a cultural explosion: the eye and the ear were separated (indeed, torn apart) by turning sound into sight. People gradually became disposed to think that 'seeing is believing', that there is a separation between mind and matter, between the heart and the head, between emotions and the intellect. Habitual reading created people who were detached, critical, even skeptical. It also created people who placed a high value upon the ability to quantify, to control, and to manage the world of external things. Print technology extended technological thinking.

But electronic technologies of today's communication methods might be drawing people back toward the culture of tribalism. Electronic media bring and implosion. Television, radio, the telephone, and the computer pull people back together. Print technology separates people (a person reads alone, thinks alone, reflects alone). Electronic media emphasize the sense of hearing, but the media bring people together because people are able to hear the same things, sometimes over great distances. People still read, but they get information and entertainment primarily from the telephone, television, radio. Especially television pulls people toward a new sensory pattern because of the low definition of a television picture and its two-dimensionality. Viewers **must** participate in what they are seeing on television because the technology of the medium forces them to fill in the spaces and contours of the picture with their imaginations.

Television also manages to integrate sight with sound, and when it does so, it creates a strong pull upon people which draws them into a cultural order different both from the pre-literate tribalism of the distant past and from the literate culture of the immediate past. Television not only reduces the family circle to a semi-circle around the television set, it entices those who watch it to participate by doing the mental act of filling in the picture. Moreover, when people watch a television program, they participate with millions of others who are having the same seeing and hearing experiences. Mass participation in the immediacy of television is not unlike the participation in the immediacy of the stories told to pre-literate people. The technology of television extends people, however, because they participate not only by hearing but by seeing. Electronic technology changes people. And it determines how they feel, how they think, and how they make choices about living. Technology creates its own culture.

Human Freedom and the Culture of Technology

Important questions are raised by the view that it is the culture of technology that determines how people are to live. And the questions are troubling: Are people free to choose how they will live if it is the technological culture which determines life? If people are **not** free to choose, how can they be held responsible for what they do? Moreover, if technological determinism is the case, what control might people be able to exercise over technological changes themselves? Or can't they?

Many thinkers wish to distinguish between the Hard Technological Determinism answer to such questions and a Soft Technological Determinism answer. The Hard Technological Determinism (HTD) holds that changes in technology provide both sufficient and necessary conditions for social change (in short, once a technology appears, not only **can** social change take place, it **will** take place). The HTD view maintains that technology today dominates all of what people consider to be modern living and that there exist no alternatives to the culture which it creates. People in India, China or Malaysia **will** like the culture of technology, they will **want** it, and they will soon find themselves **living** according to its dictates.

Soft Technological Determinism (STD), on the

other hand, is the view insisting that cultural values other than those determined by technology remain in the minds of people today, but that technology both **precipitates** the significant changes taking place in the modern world **and** it sets the range of choices about how people are going to live. For example, it remains possible to reject air conditioning, clean water, electricity, television, and the telephone, but hardly anyone **will** reject them if they are given them. Or, for example, a Soft Determinist might happily admit that a space shuttle creates a whole new range of possibilities for exploration, discovery, and development of outer space; but, he will insist, **it is not necessary** that all of the possibilities need to be attempted (yet some of them might be).

In other words, the Soft Determinist holds that technology provides necessary conditions for change, but not sufficient conditions for change (prior cultural value commitments might force significant alterations in what a technological innovation seems to require). Soft Technological Determinists think that traditional cultural values, habits mythologies, and religions play a role in the choices made among the range of changes brought by technology. Soft Determinists cite as evidence for their view the fact that identical technological developments in different cultures do not bring about identical changes. Airports in Saudi Arabia do not bring cocktail lounges into Saudi cities. Contraceptive technology in the villages of India do not significantly alter sexual mores.[4]

Some thinkers in the humanities are convinced that the ability of traditional cultures to frustrate the march of technological advance is good. For them a Brave New World is being held at bay by cultural values which will not tolerate all of the opportunities for change which new technologies present to people. Yet others think that technological thinking and acting in the present era remain too much under the control not of values of rational efficiency but of familiar human desires for comfort, wealth, excitement, profit, and power. They think that it is too often the familiar old motive of greed that frustrates the rational, efficient, and organized efforts of technologists to solve enduring problems. In short, there is no orthodox or established view about technology held by people who read and write about art, literature, and philosophy.

But the issue of the extent to which people are driven and determined by technology is a troubling one for many thinkers in the humanities. Most adopt a STD stance, claiming that alternatives for change do remain under the control of people because the sufficient conditions to bring about change (factors such as the values of tradition, myth, and religion) continue to matter to people. But if Soft Determinism is the case, it means that people must **decide** about the use, the non-use, or the misuse of technologies. To decide not to decide is still to decide. The present situation is that a whole new range of possibilities is being opened by new technology; but decisions about what technologies might be good and what technologies might be bad require attention.

References

1. Langdon Winner, *Autonomous Technology*, 1977.
2. See Jacques Ellul, *The Technological Society*, 1964, and *The Technological System*, 1980.
3. Teilhard de Chardin, *The Divine Milieu*, 1965. Aurobindo

Ghose labelled the condition 'supermind'. A discussion of Aurobindo's treatment of technology appears in Chapter 5.

4. An extended discussion of the HTD and STD positions is to be found in Robert E. McGinn, *Science, Technology, and Society*, 1991.

2

How India was made English to Make it Modern

INDIA was introduced to an early (some today might say primitive) culture of technology through the rule of Great Britain, particularly during the last seventy-five years of British rule. A major concern of some British officials since the early nineteenth century had been to make India as English as possible. Efforts were made to turn Indians into Englishmen. But along with a transfcrmation of Indians into Englishmen, there also occurred a transformation of Indians into people inclined toward the emerging culture of technology.

The crucial ingredient in such a transformation of India was English education. To understand modern Indian thought a person must understand the crucial role that English education was made to play in the lives of India's intellectuals. British rulers became convinced that Indians were to be impressed not only with the culture of the West but with the wonders that its technology might bring.

But, it is important to remember that many important Indian thinkers held extremely negative views of English language, literature, and history. A thinker as significant as Aurobindo Ghose called British education "the English web". Gandhi thought it a "blighting imposition" which "sapped the energy of the nation". Jawaharlal Nehru insisted that it had turned him into "a queer mixture of East and West, out of place everywhere, at home nowhere."

These Indians were convinced that the British system of education ordered and organized to assist in making servants for British rulers could do little more than provide Indians with skills to assist their masters. Yet, strangely enough, these men (queer mix that they might have been) were the same who could argue persuasively and effectively that self-rule and knowledge of an Indian culture was the birthright of every Indian. An education designed with the hope of producing clerks instilled at the same time the important technological values of rationality, efficiency, organization, and standardization. Indian students discovered that a person cannot long remain rational and at the same time insist that race or birth or religion have anything at all to do with intelligence, competence, or expertise. So an education designed to produce clerks instead produced thinkers committed to modernization, to industrialism, to progress, in short, to a culture of technology. And those thinkers educated to be servants led a successful revolt against British rule.

The story of what might be seen as something of a British bungle is complicated. What was intended to cement a hold on India instead worked to loosen that hold. Yet more complicated is the story of how Indian thinkers worked to synthesize traditional cultural ideals with Western commitments to a culture of technology. How clerks might be made into fire brand nationalists is one story. How these Indians might argue about education and culture is another.

Education and Company Policy

Controversies over education and culture had roots in the eighteenth century reforms of the British East India Company's involvement in India. In spite of the fact that Great Britain dominated all trading markets in India, Parliament ordered Governor-General Warren Hastings to reform the Company when he was sent to lead it in 1772. Reform under Hastings was an effort to 'orientalize' the service by encouraging British employees of the Company to learn Indian languages and to conform to Indian customs. Reform measures supported such study by offering advancement to those who could translate Company policies and procedures into an Indian language. Hastings himself led the way by developing proficiency in Bengali and Urdu, together with Persian, the language of the Muslim courts.

But mastery of Indian languages did not simply open the way to professional advancement for employees. Language study also introduced some Englishmen to the literatures of traditional India. Of particular importance was the discovery of the ancient language of Sanskrit.

The discovery of Sanskrit literature led some East India Company employees to the conclusion that somewhere in a remote and uncharted past lay a Golden Age of Indian culture. 'Orientalist' enthusiasts like Sir William Jones, William Colbrooke, and Charles Wilkins concluded from their investigations that Sanskrit might be the fountainhead of many languages. Sanskrit, in Jones' words, was a language "more perfect than Greek, more copious than Latin, and more exquisitely refined than either, yet bearing to both of them a stronger affinity both in the roots of verbs and the form of grammar than could possibly have been produced by accident."[1]

Jones linked Sanskrit to the culture of Europe. He maintained that it was not possible for him to read the ancient Indian texts without believing "that Pythagoras and Plato derived their sublime theories from the same fountain with the sages of India".[2]

As tentative as such conclusions might have been, the research into India's past made a profound impression upon both Englishmen and Indians. The studies by Englishmen contrasted a Sanskrit "age of gold" with the society of their own time. India possessed a Golden Age of culture, it was said. But such an age lay buried beneath centuries of neglect. The ancient Indians had been outgoing and non-mystical. They had been a robust, meat-eating, socially equalitarian people. In place of despotic governments, there had been tribal republics. Religion was monotheistic. And there was no evidence of image worship, temples, or the mistreatment of women.

What is remarkable is that discoveries of a Golden Age of the second millennium B.C.E. conjured a whole new image of India both for Englishmen and for many Indians. Former British scholarship which had denigrated Indian culture, now seemed to be suggesting that India had a cultural history which needed revival. And a significant consequence for Indians was that they were provided an historical theory making sense of their past, in much the way Europeans made some sense of their own past. The theory maintained that there had been a Golden Age of a great and noble culture. But the Golden Age had not endured. A Dark Age of priestly misguidance and/or Muslim interference (the theory itself did not establish blame) obliterated earlier achievements.

The implied task of Indian intellectuals was to revive

antiquity through a recovery of the language, literature and art of the Golden Age. Conclusions generated by Company scholarship provided a motive for the resurgence and revival of Indian culture. And it did not matter to many Indians, under the circumstances, whether the categories of 'Golden Age', 'Dark Age', or 'Renaissance' actually fit the data of Indian history. Nor did it matter who had made the discoveries. There had been an age of gold. And that age needed rediscovery.

Yet British support for a cultural revitalization of India found little support among Imperialists in England. In fact, agitation against Hastings' programme of 'Orientalism' began almost as soon as it started. Opponents argued that 'Anglicization' of Indians, not 'Orientalization' of Englishmen, should be the goal of Imperialism.

Agitation came from two movements in British society — the one committed the Christian religion, the other to the philosophical foundations of the culture of technology. The religious movement was Evangelical Christianity. The philosophical views known as Utilitarianism provided the base for the culture of technology. Although the two groups drew inspiration from opposed conceptual schemes (Christian piety on the one hand and secular hedonism on the other), they shared an antipathy toward traditional Indian culture.

Evangelical Christians directed their strongest arguments against the Orientalist view that the British East India Company should avoid interference with Indian religious life. Charles Grant (an advisor to Cornwallis during the 1780s and later Chairman of the Court of Directors for the Company) argued that the moral improvement of Indian society was as much a responsibility of the Company as was commercial success.

Grant mixed religion and economics into an argument
that was convincing to many members of Parliament.

> In considering the affairs of the world as
> under the control of the Supreme Disposer,
> and those distant territories providentially
> put into our hands ... is it not necessary to
> conclude that they were given to us, not
> merely that we might draw an annual
> profit from them, but that we might diffuse
> among their inhabitants, long sunk in
> darkness, vice, and misery the light and
> benign influence of the truth, the blessings
> of a well-regulated society, the improve-
> ments and comforts of an active industry?
> ... In every progressive step of this work
> we shall also serve the original design still
> so important to this country — the
> extension of our commerce.[3]

Evangelicals such as Charles Grant and William
Wilberforce dismissed the religious traditions of India
as "one grand abomination". Moreover, because India's
religions were to them degrading, the whole culture
must be barbaric, they though. To tolerate such a
culture was to their minds a violation of Christian
morality.

Consequently, the Evangelicals proposed a policy of
cultural change for India. The British were to be agents
of that change. By living and working among Indians
and by establishing educational and religious
institutions, the moral uplift of Indians might be
accomplished.

Let us endeavour to strike our roots into

the soil . . . by the gradual introduction and
establishment of our principles and
opinions; of our laws and institutions; and
. . . above all, as the source of every other
improvement, of our religion and
consequently of our morals.[4]

Grant recommended the introduction of Christianity
not simply as a religion but as a useful means to re-shape
Indian culture:

It is not . . . the introduction of a new set of
ceremonies, nor even a new creed, that is
the ultimate object here. Those who con-
ceive religion to be conversant merely
about forms and speculative motives, may
well think that the world need not be much
troubled concerning it. No, the ultimate
object is moral improvement. The pre-
eminent excellence of the morality which
the Gospel teaches, and the superior
efficacy of this divine system, taken in all
its parts, in meliorating the conditions of
human society, cannot be denied by those
who are unwilling to admit its higher
claims; and on this ground only, the
dissemination of it must be beneficial to
mankind.[5]

To promote research into India's past was not only
wasted effort, according to Grant, it was an indication
of a moral failure on the part of the British. To encourage
a flirtation with the languages and culture of India
jeopardized the moral progress not only of India but of
England herself.

Utilitarians, a second group opposed to the Orientalist programme but intensely committed to the improvements new technology might bring to India, actually sought the same goal of moral uplift, but by different means. Utilitarians believed that morals could be improved not by the introduction of a new religion but by social measures of education and modernization. Education must be a crucial instrument to bring about change. But for thinkers such as Jeremy Bentham and James Mill, an education 'useful' and 'instrumental' for social change could not be one which concentrated upon India's past, however glorious that might have been. A useful education must consist of methods and ideas to re-shape the present so that progress might be achieved. Utilitarians could hold but little sympathy for Evangelical Christianity. But they held no sympathy whatsoever for any program which might be devoted to reinstating the past. What India needed was modernization — technological development. And modern technology could not be found in ancient texts. It could be found only in the application of science to the problems which were seen to plague British India.

James Mill in his multi-volume *History of British India* (1818) formulated what was then in England a basic Liberal attitude toward traditional Indian culture. He explored India's past in terms of Utilitarian assumptions concerning what was useful, helpful, and progressive. He did not argue a specific case for Westernization (as the Evangelicals did); but he did argue that there was neither anything useful nor uplifting in traditional Indian culture. In fact, he maintained, Hastings' programme of Orientalism had done a disservice to India, because by calling attention to India's past, nothing had been done to eradicate the conditions of the present population which might be remedied by the introduction of modern technology.

So Mill substituted a dismal picture of ancient India for the Orientalist image of a Golden Age. He argued that beneath a veneer of achievements mentioned by Orientalists there lay a primitive and barbaric society held together by political despotism and priestcraft. And he maintained that such tyranny had produced an irrational, inefficient, and morally deficient society.

> Even in manners, and in the leading parts of the moral character, the lines of resemblance between Indians and Chinese are strong. Both nations are to nearly an equal degree tainted with the vices of insincerity, dissembling, and treacherous, mendacious, to an excess which surpass even the usual measure of an uncultivated society. Both are disposed to excessive exaggeration with regard to everything related to themselves. Both are cowardly and unfeeling. Both are to the highest degree conceited of themselves, and full of contempt for others. Both are in a physical sense disgustingly unclean in their persons and houses.[6]

The racist and imperialist prejudices of Mill ought not to cloud the fact that he was genuinely distressed because Englishmen had done little to solve problems of poverty and illness which he thought modern technology might address. In addition, Mill insisted that there was something morally wrong with Imperialist business practices: measures of reform should end a Company monopoly, should end the whole notion of 'chartered companies', and they should put an end to traditional

Indian customs regarding property rights. Indian, he
insisted, must be opened to capitalist enterprise based
on wholesome competition. Moreover, Indian must be
introduced to a 'useful' literature, a free press, and to the
colonization of British merchants and industries. The
culture of technology, Mill was saying, does not tolerate
a hierarchical society based upon traditional categories
of authority or merit; and it will not tolerate a traditional
literature irrelevant to practical affairs. The solution,
he maintained, was the establishment of a free press
which might allow the general distribution of new ideas
and values. A modern reader must conclude that Mill
ear a champion of the new culture of democracy and
technology.

That Mill had never touched Indian soil, together
with his heavy reliance upon secondary source material
to back his derogatory remarks about Indian culture,
inspired elaborate rebuttals from scholars familiar with
Indian culture. Yet Mill's view of India triumphed
because Governor-General William Bentinck and
Thomas Babington Macaulay went to India convinced
by Mill's *History*. Bentinck confessed to Mill in 1872, "I
am going to British India, but I shall not be Governor-
General. It is you that will be Governor-General".[7]

Bentinck appointed T.B. Macaulay president of the
General Committee of Public Instruction in Calcutta.
Macaulay broke what had been a deadlocked education
policy. Espousing 'Progressive' principles of liberty,
equality, and economic prosperity to be values of
universal importance, Macaulay insisted that such values
be imported to India. Yet, at the same time, he was
convinced that "the English have become the greatest
and most highly civilized people ever the world saw. . . ."[8]

Macaulay tied modernization representative government, and social progress directly to the genius of the English people. Though a latent racism underlies his statements, it was his arrogance which distressed both Indian and Orientalist readers of his famous "Minute on Education" of 1835.

> I have never found one among them [the Orientalists] who could deny that a single shelf of a good European library was worth the whole native literature of India. . . . [9]

Government support for educational institutions and materials of little use for development in social and economic matters was to Macaulay absurd,

> . . . to encourage the study of a literature admitted to be of small intrinsic value, only because that literature inculcates the most serious errors on the most important subjects, is a course hardly reconcilable with reason, with morality, or even with the very neutrality which ought, as we all agree, to be sacredly preserved. It is confessed that a language is barren of useful knowledge. We are to teach it because it is fruitful of monstrous superstitions. We are to teach false history, false astronomy, false medicine, because we find them in company with a false religion.[10]

Education that concentrated upon Indian culture Macaulay believed to be useless for life in the modern world. But the English language and a Western education were closely joined to the sources of modern economic theory, to modern political theory, and to a new culture of technology. And it was apparent to Macaulay that some Indians serving English masters desired to learn English, since it was a vehicle to promotion in a society governed by the British. Finally, since it might be possible to make some Indians into men of a practical proficiency (indeed, some might even become scholars), it was in the long term interest of Great Britain to convert Indians into Englishmen.

Macaulay wrote,

> We must do our best to form a class who may be interpreters between us and the millions whom we govern, a class of persons Indian in blood and colour, but English in taste, in opinions, in morals and in intellect.[11]

The Education Act of 1835 by Parliament solidified the Macaulay position. It was decided that an education in English for Indians was to be the route to progress and development for India. In 1837 English replaced Persian as the official language of the courts. In 1844 Lord Hardinge's administration announced that those educated in English would be preferred in all appointments to the Indian Civil Service. Under government support and promise of promotion, a degree from an English institution of learning became the accepted object of ambition for Indians, the passport to public service and to the professions. For example, of the 1589 students in the Bengal Presidency who earned arts degrees in the University of Calcutta between 1857 and 1882, 526 entered public service, 581 entered the legal profession, and 12 became medical doctors. The remaining served as teachers in the schools and colleges of India. Eventually, anyone who had taken a degree from an English school or even passed the entrance examination was found to possess considerably enhanced value in the marriage market. In short, Indian society embraced English education.

The Revival of Indian Culture

But the study of English language, literature, and history brought its own peculiar contradictions. Lord Curzon entered India as the twenty-fourth Governor-General in 1898 convinced that the foremost cause of unrest among Indians was "the education we have given to the people of the country".

A significant element in the agitation against British rule during Curzon's time was English education itself — the education that provided Indians the values of rationality, objectivity, measurement, efficiency, and expertise. Along with those values, of course, were to be found also the values of independence, equal opportunity, democracy, and the ideals of an emerging culture of technology. The agitation was often organized by young men who wanted to re-educate themselves about India and her tradition. And in doing so, those Indians revived the Orientalist theory of a bygone Golden Age of culture.

Aurobindo Ghose (1872-1950), an arts graduate of Cambridge University, returned to India to denounce English schools, and to call for "an unravelling of the English web, a retracing of the steps toward perdition which we were forced or induced to take". Submission to a British curriculum had blotted out India's past and had tightened the hold of the British Government. Aurobindo called for a boycott of everything British, especially education.

Mohandas K. Gandhi arrived in India after his legal work in South Africa dismayed to find the educated

classes of India out of touch with their own culture an
unable in the most literal sense to speak to the masses.

> Among the many evils of foreign rule this
> blighting imposition of a foreign medium
> upon the youth of the country will be
> counted by history as one of the greatest.
> It has sapped the energy of the nation. . . .
> It has estranged them from the masses
> . . . . The sooner therefore educated India
> shakes itself free from the hypnotic spell
> of the foreign medium, the better it will be
> for them and the people.[12]

And Nehru, a man destined to lead the independent
nation after 1947, insisted, "I have become a queer
mixture of East and West, out of place every where, at
home nowhere; I cannot get rid of either that past
inheritance or my recent acquisitions".[13]

This 'queer mixture' was a British-sponsored period
of self-discovery for Indians. But the wherewithal to
establish foundations for a return to greatness was
removed by the decision to educate Indians in English
and in the ideas and values of an industrial society (the
new culture of technology).

The modern history of India is tinged with this
curious mix: efforts to revive a Golden Age go hand in
hand with appeals to ideals of progress and technological
advance. One must ask, might such a mix might be the
answer to the sterility of the culture of technology as it
is thought by many to exist among Western nations?
But one must ask as well, how long might such a mix as
India has achieved last? And, how long might Indians
wish it to last?

References

1. *Asiatic Researches* (1788), pp.422-23.
2. *Ibid.*, p. 424.
3. Speech reproduced in *Charles Grant and British Rule in India,* ed. by Ainslie Thomas Embree, pp.141-57.
4. *Substance of the Speeches of William Wilberforce Esq. on the Causes in the East India Bill for Promoting the Religious Instruction and Moral Improvement of the Natives of the British Dominions in India,* p. 92.
5. Quoted in Embree, p. 99.
6. James Mill, *History of British India,* II, p.135.
7. Quoted in Eric Stokes, *The English Utilitarians and India,* p. 51.
8. Thomas Babington Macaulay, "On Sir James Mackintosh".
9. *Ibid.*, "Minute on Education".
10. *Ibid.*
11. *Ibid.*
12. Mohandas K. Gandhi, *True Education,* pp. 96-100.
13. Jawaharlal Nehru, *Toward Freedom,* p. 353.

3

Mahatma Gandhi and the
Culture of Technology

IT was the nationalist hero Mohandas K. Gandhi who
raised what might be the fundamental question about
modern scientific technology. He raised the question,
however, in a context of nationalist agitation against
British imperialism. Gandhi maintained that India
must be free of British rule; but he insisted that freedom
as he understood it was more than political independence.
For India to be free the people of India must realize
independence from a whole system, a whole way of life,
which he insisted was immoral, exploitative, unjust,
and dishonest. And it was at this point that Gandhi's
concern for a free India raised for him fundamental
questions about modern technology.

In short, the political question about whether India
had a right to independence from British rule presupposed an answer to a prior question about the way of
life imposed by foreign rule. The prior question was a
moral question concerning how people ought to live. For
Gandhi political philosophy and moral philosophy were
identical. Great Britain was imposing upon India a way
of life contrary to Indian tradition **and** to proper morality.

Not only must Great Britain as a ruling power be resisted but the way of life promoted by Great Britain must be resisted, too. And a fundamental difficulty about the way of life promoted by Great Britain was that it was shot through with commitments to the culture of technology.

So Gandhi's thinking about modern technology was tied to the issue of national freedom. And because the two issues were for Gandhi synonymous, the issue of national freedom was one not simply of replacing one set of government officials with another set, but an issue of replacing one way of life with another way of life, one morality with another. Gandhi as a social philosopher and activist, then, was confronted with a problem greater than ordinary revolutionaries usually confront. The question for Gandhi was whether it might be possible for a 'radical' problem (a problem more extensive and complex than who should govern the country) to be resolved by an appeal to 'moderate' means of resolution.[1]

The problem was radical in the sense that Gandhi believed that it was the way of life imposed upon Indian from the outside which needed to be replaced by another way of life. A radical solution to such a problem would necessarily involve violent revolution followed by efforts to eliminate remnants of the foreign ways (much in the way Mao Tse Tung in China acted first to resist foreign rule, then to resist remnants of foreign ways of the *Kuomintang* sympathizers. And finally to promote a cultural revolution among Chinese the people).

But a moderate solution to the radical problem India faced required that Indians find some means by which the British could be convinced that it is in their best interests to leave India so that India could be free to be India. It is important to keep in mind that the problem for India was radical because it was both political and cultural. Foreign rule went hand in hand with efforts to subvert traditional Indian culture through English education. 'Macaulayism' was a commitment as early as 1835 to "form a class . . . of persons, Indian in blood and colour, but English in taste, in opinions, in morals, and in intellect".[2] An English education meant for Indians a chance for employment in the empire; but it meant as well the abandonment of an educated appreciation or commitment to traditional Indian culture. Indians who wished to advance in the empire were required to study the language and literature that served as a foundation for scientific technology. And the languages of traditional India (however refined they might have been) were ignored or reduced to vernacular languages in the minds of those who wished to advance in British India.

Requirements for a moderate solution to the radical problem of political and cultural subjugation required a resolution which might come about through an appeal to ideas and values implicit to all aspects of the problem — that is to say, to ideas and values basic to Indian tradition, to modern technology, to ideals of British political order, and to ideals of Indian political order. The British, with all of the force of a conquering government, had done what they could to replace Indian culture with British culture. The question facing a moderate such as Gandhi, then, was whether there might be a way to join Indian tradition with modern technology at the same time as Indian political ideals could be joined with British political ideals.

Reduced to bare bones, the Gandhian proposal for a moderate resolution to the radical problem consisted of an identification of the problem of Indian subjugation not with the British Government in India but more

fundamentally with what he saw to be British tendencies
to 'immorality'. For Gandhi, the British Government in
India was a present manifestation to India of an issue
more complex than the issue of politics. And his proposal
reduced the political issue of freedom and cultural issue
of how best to live to just one issue: the demise of Indian
freedom and the demise of its traditional way of life
occurred through a capitulation to the seductive evils of
an immoral culture. For Gandhi, complex political
issues were to be best understood as in the first instance
moral matters about how people ought to live.

But for Gandhi's proposal to be a moderate resolution
to the radical problem, he needed first to clarify ideas
and values fundamental to both British and Indian
culture. The fundamental denominator of both cultures
Gandhi identified to be a commitment to morality as the
chief end of human endeavour. Then, using the notion
of morality as a value basic both to the English and to
Indians, Gandhi asserted an ethic contrary to what he
suspected British culture to be advancing. And finally,
he devised a method of political action to counter the
evils of this foreign culture. In short, Gandhi's critique
is that Great Britain (indeed, all of the Western nations)
abandoned an earlier commitment to a rational morality
by adopting a culture of technology. Implicit to his
critique is an assertion that morality and modern
technology are at odds. And implicit as well is a suggestion
that the culture of technology forces the abandonment of
morality.

Morality and the Nature of Truth

The groundwork for Gandhi's solution to India's problem
lay in his appeal to what is in fact an essentially Western
notion of moral perfection as the chief end of human life.[3]

Gandhi agreed with the mainstream of Western thought that the highest value for human life is realization of moral perfectibility within the limits of human rational powers. And with this assumption, he placed with himself on a footing which insured for him the possibility of a moderate resolution to the political problem at hand. Gandhi was convinced that an appeal to morality is an appeal to mutually affirmed convictions about the purposes and ends of social order.

Much of Gandhi's writing about the political situation of rule by Great Britain was directed toward what he saw to be the defection of Western thinkers from the proper goal of existence. His writing was structured to expose over and over again the British defection from the path leading to the proper goal. Then he worked to show that a return to Indian tradition might be a solution to the debilitating effects of cultural imperialism.

In an early work, *Hind Swaraj* (1908), written while still engaged in his South African work, Gandhi claimed, "It is my deliberate opinion that India is being ground down, not under the English heel but under that of modern civilization."[4] The civilization advanced by the West he saw to be aimed at making bodily comfort the goal for living rather than making morality the goal. The fundamental issue separating Indian and European interests, then, was first one of how people ought to live in relation to what is really important. Political considerations were to be regarded as incidental to that fundamental issue, an issue of culture. But since commitment to bodily comfort is contrary to the proper goal of human existence, such a commitment, if it were to spread everywhere, might threaten the moral fabric of all human society. Gandhi considered all of the evils which might be associated with the rule of India by

Great Britain to follow from this prior commitment of
the West to advance technology devoted to comfort and
ease. Gandhi wrote about the culture of technology with
some disparagement:

> Let us first consider what state of things is
> described by the word 'civilization'. Its
> true test lies in the fact that people living
> in it make bodily welfare the object of life
> . . . . The people of Europe today live in
> better-built houses than they did a hundred
> years ago. This is considered an emblem
> of civilization, and this is also a matter to
> promote bodily happiness. . . . Formerly, in
> Europe, people ploughed their lands
> mainly by manual labour. Now one man
> can plough a vast tract by means of steam
> engines and can thus amass great wealth.
> This is called a sign of civilization. . . .
> Formerly men travelled in waggons (*sic*).
> Now, they fly through the air in trains at
> the rate of four hundred and more miles
> per day. This is considered the height of
> civilization. . . . Formerly when people
> wanted to fight with one another, they
> measured between them their bodily
> strength; now it is possible to take away
> thousands of lives by one man working
> behind a gun from a hill. This is
> civilization.[5]

Technology morally debases human beings. The process
of debasement results from capitulation to the promises
of ease and comfort which modern technology promotes.
India is subservient to the British not because England
is a great military and economic power or because

Englishmen are intellectually superior to Indians. India is subservient because Indians have sold out to the values of technology.

> The English have not taken India, we have given it to them. They are not in India because of their strength, but because we keep them. ... We keep the English in India for our base self-interest. We like their commerce; they please us by their subtle methods and get what they want from us.[6]

The immorality of technological culture is to be found in the subtle re-definition of values which it promotes. And in promoting the values it does, technology manages to eliminate from the minds of people the proper sense of how they should live. The process empties traditional values of old meanings and re-fills them with new meanings. Courage once meant pitting oneself against others in physical combat. Now it has a new meaning associated with new tools which allow a person to destroy others from a distance. Charity once meant giving of oneself; now it has been re-defined as giving of ones's excess. Truth once was a recognition of reality (they way things are); now it has been defined as a property of a proposition (a construction of language, an ordering of words).

Since the evils of imperialism are merely consequences of capitulation to the fundamental evil of a whole misguided culture, to merely rid India of Englishmen will not solve the major problem. In fact, to use the modern techniques of the British to drive them from India would be to embrace the very evil which must be expelled from India. Such a solution could be no solution at all: it would pattern India after England, it would turn Hindustan into 'Englistan'.[7]

> It is not necessary for us to have as our goal the expulsion of the English. If the English become Indianized, we can accommodate them. If they wish to remain in India along with their civilization there is no room for them.[8]

Because it is the culture which the British have imported to India that is evil, it follows that one task of an Indian nationalist is to clarify the spheres of good and evil. Implied in Gandhi's thinking is the conviction that a complete rejection of evil would mean a rejection of the culture of technology and its moral and epistemological foundations.[9]

In the place of science, Gandhi asserted what he thought to be an authentically Indian epistemology, an epistemology committed to discovering truth to be fundamentally a moral issue. To seek knowledge, he maintained, is to seek truth. But truth is a dimension of human experience involving an effort to establish a certain relationship to reality. In short, Gandhi would deny any notion of truth as strictly empirical or rational, truth as propositional, or truth as a language construct. Truth is not simply the property of a proposition which corresponds to certain facts. Propositions are human constructs, they are creations of language. Truth is the property of a proper relationship to reality, to the way things are.

What is important to Gandhi's view of the nature of truth is that he settles the concept of truth-seeking solidly into the sphere of ethics. Truth is an experienced relation to the world and to other people. It is most clearly a property of a relationship between persons. When people open themselves to one another, they experience truth (which is to say that they experience reality).

Gandhi did not hesitate to identify truth in this sense (*satya*) with God.

> There are innumerable definitions of God, because His manifestations are innumerable. But I worship God as Truth only.[10]

Gandhi considered the discipline of searching for and realizing truth to be a 'holding to truth' or a 'grasping after truth' (*satyagraha*). But in such searching person is searching for God.

> I do not regard God as a Person. Truth for me is God, and God's Law and God are not different things or facts, in the sense that an earthly king and his law are different .... Truth in Sanskrit means *sat*. *Sat* means 'is'. Therefore the more truthful we are, the nearer we are to God. We 'are' only to the extent that we are truthful.[11]

For Gandhi, the proper method for discovering truth as relational is crucial. It is *ahimsa*, non-violence. Non-violence and grasping after truth (*satyagraha*) are so close to one another that they are "two sides of a coin". Whereas truth is ultimately absolute, human understanding or grasp of it is partial and relative. Therefore no one is justified in dogmatically asserting one particular view of what is true. Neither ought a person to use force (violence) to promote a particular view of what is true. Searching for truth and holding to a particular conception of truth must always be non-violent. And any procedure for discovering truth must maintain a constant openness to correction, modification, and persuasion which will renounce even the will to damage or to harm.

The test for certification of truth (verification) in any human encounter is the test of openness, an openness willing to accept the possible truth of another viewpoint and the possible falseness of one's own viewpoint. A person finds certitude concerning truth only by noting whether or not communication with someone who disagrees is maintained. Again, the method of verification testifies to the fact that truth is finally relational, not propositional.

Where there is disagreement among people concerning truth, non-violence must be steadily maintained as a method of discovering what is really true. Sometimes non-violence must shade into *tapasya*, self-suffering. Traditionally *tapasya* stood for self-restraint, self-discipline, and self-control as a part of yogic discipline. For Gandhi *tapasya* stood for the self-control required in opening oneself to others, especially when such openness might invite anger, or hatred, or violence. *Tapasya* involves inviting suffering upon oneself for the purpose of convincing others of truth. In political controversies *tapasya* often must take the form of civil disobedience. In this sense it constitutes inviting suffering if suffering might be a way to point up the immorality (untruth) of a law or condition in society. A person ought to invite cheerfully the penalty of a law while simultaneously resisting the law by consciously violating it.

All of this Gandhi asserted as a way of living and thinking quite opposed to the culture of technology. The scientific foundation of modern technology puts a premium not simply upon knowledge that is empirically demonstrable, but upon knowledge that is useful; and the technologies that follow from useful knowledge divert people from the proper goal of living and direct them instead toward what can be enjoyed. The fact of India's dependence and enslavement was an indication that India had capitulated to modern technology. Political independence by itself, therefore, would be no solution. Instead, India must first return to its authentic tradition, its own identity, to its own reality (*sat*). To adopt a foreign culture, especially a culture devoted to immorality, could be no solution.

Truth-seeking and Political Activity

Truth-seeking is first a way of proper living. But the application of the Gandhian method of truth-seeking to the political sphere will follow inevitably. The application is done by equating ends and means. If the end of human existence is an open recognition and a relationship to what is real (truth), the proper end of human existence is morality. But if the end or goal of living morality, it makes sense that the means to that end must be moral, too. For Gandhi this meant that because the method for realizing truth is moral, so too the method for realizing political independence must be moral. Means must correspond to ends, since ends and means do not really differ. If the end is morality, the means to that end must be moral means. Violence, cruelty, and abuse cannot and will not ever bring about a moral consequence. It is wrong to think that an end might be used to justify means.

A result of such reasoning for Gandhi was for him the conclusion that non-violence must be the ordinary means to bring about any end. But such a requirement need not complicate the movement for national independence, in Gandhi's view. Instead, it simplified it. Nationalist workers need to be concerned only to reveal by non-violent means both truth and untruth wherever it might exist. How to do such a thing is simply a matter of being open to reality. There need be no distinction between knowing and doing, between ends and means, between theory and action.

India as a subject nation, then, could find itself relieved of many complications. Indians had been made slaves in their own country. But they were made slaves because they capitulated to the untruth that India belonged to Englishmen. A proper relationship to what is really the case would bring a return to self-rule (because truth would require the recognition that India is India, not England). For Gandhi, a necessary consequence of opening oneself to reality (*sat*, being, truth) must be to recognize that India is for Indians. He said, "It is not necessary for us to have as our goal the expulsion of the English. If the English become Indianized, we can accommodate them."

Truth-seeking and Life with Technology

Gandhi's views about technology follow from his commitments to truth and morality. And his remarks about technology were often extremely critical. Yet it might be important for a contemporary reader to note that when Gandhi made his remarks about technology, life was very different from the sort of life that technology permits today. When Gandhi wrote and spoke there were no jet airplanes, no computers, no microwave ovens, no electric typewriters, no word processors, no tape recorders, no stereo music systems, no fluorescent lights, no VCRs, no air conditioning, no credit cards, no synthetic fibers, no antibiotics, no artificial organs, no pesticides, and no herbicides.

But there **were** industries, and there was industrial production of mass produced goods, and all of it was being moving into india. Industrial development moved people from the villages to the cities, and eventually to the slums. Yet at the same time, it must be kept in mind that when Gandhi was writing about industry there was no widespread concern about environmental pollution, about over-populated cities, about radiation exposure, about nuclear war, about ozone depletion. Nor were there reasons to consider the moral implications of contraceptive technologies, *in vitro* fertilization technologies, organ procurement and transplant technologies, or drug technologies that significantly alter the lives of people.

In short, Gandhi wrote about technology at a time when most of the advantages as well as the complications of technology either did not exist or were not yet recognized as problems. In fact, when Gandhi made his earliest comments to warn Indians and Englishmen about technology (in the book *Hind Swaraj*) he set himself directly **against** popular attitudes of optimism — even euphoria — concerning what technology might be able to accomplish for mankind. Many people today find what Gandhi was remarkably prescient about problems which were to follow from the basic industrial technologies of his time.

The force of Gandhi's message lies in his rejection of what he saw to be the culture of the modern world. Modern culture — the culture of technology — was for Gandhi a positive menace to morality. The technological achievements of the modern world confuse people and deflect them from proper concerns about morality. Gandhi's concern about technology may stem from a sensitivity to a traditional Hindu teaching of *maya*, 'illusion'. He maintained that the culture of technology is a threat because it creates a false sense of what is important, indeed, of what is real. Modern technology functions much like a narcotic, a drug or an anesthetic to desensitize, deaden and numb the minds of people. Technological innovations trick people and entice them toward a path of self-destruction. Gandhi noted that the fascination of the Western world for technology was a mental illness. "This civilization is irreligion and it has taken such a hold on the people of Europe that those who are in it appear to be half mad."[12]

Yet because Gandhi admitted the usefulness of some machinery (particularly the spinning wheel), his remarks must be put into the context of his fight for independence from what he saw to be a foreign culture. In fact, because Gandhi admitted the usefulness of some machinery (some technology), it might be accurate to attribute to Gandhi an important distinction between two technological cultures, one advanced by foreigners and one indigenous and traditional. Gandhi seemed to be convinced that imported technology carried its own culture, its own values, its own way of life which would be imposed upon India along with new tools and new industry. But an indigenous technology, a technology rooted in and growing out of the basic requirements of the vast majority of Indian people living in the villages, would be quite different than the technology of foreigners.

Gandhi reduced technology to moral philosophy in the same way that he reduced politics to moral philosophy. For Gandhi, technology should never be thought of as value-neutral.[13] Technology creates tools for doing things; technology, therefore, is a means to an end. But means and ends must always correspond to one another in a moral sense. Thus a technology can never be morally neutral. Any technology which might enslave people in a process of improving some conditions for them is wrong. Any technology which might de-humanize people at the same time as it brings them some comforts is wrong. Any technology which might hurt some people in order to help some other people is wrong.

Certain conclusions about technology follow from Gandhi's principle of the equation of ends and means. First, a proper technology must carry with its procedures of implementation a recognition of human equality and promise to be non-exploitative (the social implications of a technology must be to treat all people as equals, instead of allowing some to exploit others). Second, only those specific technologies which contribute to the full employment of people are morally sound (that is to say that the so-called labour-saving advantages of some technologies might be immoral because they force unemployment upon some people). Third, only those technologies which can provide low-priced consumer goods which satisfy actual **needs** of people are right and good (and it must be recognized that many technologies serve no actual human need). Forth, it is morally wrong to mass produce goods which will not be equally 'distributed to the masses (mass production technologies must be altered to be production technologies for the masses). And fifth, all sophisticated technologies requiring highly specialized machines and technicians must be publicly owned and managed.

> I would prize every invention of science made for the benefit of all. . . . I am not aiming at the eradication of all machinery,

but limitation, because the supreme
consideration is man. The machine should
not tend to make atrophied the limbs of
man.[14]

What Gandhi feared most was that a culture of technology
would be imposed upon a traditional culture in the same
way that foreign rule had been imposed upon a traditional
system of government. And even as the traditional
system of government was eliminated in favour of a
foreign system, so traditional technologies would be
eliminated in favour of the foreign technologies.

The central concepts of Gandhi, then, were Truth,
Satyagraha, and non-violence. Imbedded in those ideas
were the practical ideas of *Swadeshi* and Bread Labour.
Swadeshi quite simply meant that the people of India
must practice their freedom by doing things **for
themselves**. This had immediate implications for anyone
committed to the independence movement (he or she
must not look to the foreigners for **anything**, but he or she
must do themselves what needs to be done: wear
homespun clothing, send children to Indian schools, use
traditional arbitration methods to settle disputes, employ
only Indian businessmen, tradesmen, professionals, etc.).
Bread Labour, of course, meant that each person who
wished to live according to truth, to hold fast to the truth,
and to be non-violent must also work — honestly,
diligently, attentively, industriously. But such work
would encourage self-reliance, discipline, and even
courage. For Gandhi it meant that a person would put
into practice his or her relationship to truth, to being, to
reality as he or she understood it. And no technology
should be allowed to subvert such a **moral** commitment.

Gandhi's writing is sometimes cited by historians as
being unsystematic, sometimes erratic, and even

contradictory. But if attention is given to Gandhi's ideas in terms of his quest for complete freedom — freedom from whatever might oppress the Indian people, including technology — then he appears to have held quite a clear, rational, and compelling teaching about culture.

References

1. A study such as this requires what I wish to call "constructive analysis". It is analytical in the sense that I am fitting together what Gandhi said about this topic in such a way as to explain his ideas and what might be the limits of those ideas. But since it is the case (as we shall see) that Gandhi did not confront technology in the way in which I do today, the study must be constructive. This is to say that I wish to interpret Gandhi fairly at the same time as I maintain enough distance from the immediate issues confronting him to be able to give some attention to overall structures of thought into which his ideas fit.

2. It is true that some British officials did study Indian traditions and favoured an economy of trade based on those traditions. But such proposals were not implemented. See chapter 2.

3. I say this is an essentially Western notion of the end of human existence because of the recurring tendency of philosophers since Plato to return to the value of self-knowledge and self-control through reason as the ultimate source of any happiness within human reach. In spite of their differences, philosophers such as Aristotle, Aquinas, Locke, Hume, Kant, and even Bertrand Russell agree that morality is the highest value for humanity and that it lies in the exercise of reason for the subjugation of the passions. For better or worse, the ultimate value recognized by classical Indian thinkers is not morality but freedom, not self-control in

the interests of a community, but complete control over one's environment. See Karl H. Potter, *Presuppositions of India's Philosophies*, pp.1-24.

4. *Hind Swaraj* in *The Collected Works of Mahatma Gandhi*, Ch. X, p.24.

5. *Ibid.*, pp.19-20.

6. *Ibid.*, pp.22, 23.

7. *Ibid.*, p. 15.

8. *Ibid.*, p. 9.

9. Gandhi at this point differs from some modern Indian thinkers because he rejects modern technology in terms of its scientific foundations. Many Indian thinkers intellectually skewer themselves trying to show that authentic Indian tradition is not incompatible with science. Gandhi wanted to make it clear that the scientific foundations upon which modern technology rests are immoral.

10. M.K. Gandhi, *An Autobiography: The Story of My Experiments with Truth* (Beacon Press, 1957), p. 4.

11. Letter to P.G. Mathew, July 9, 1932, published in *Harijan*, March 27, 1949.

12. *Hind Swaraj*, Chapter IV.

13. Gandhi insisted that there could be no positivist, non-normative science dealing with the lives of human beings. In short, he rejected the objective, positivist pretensions of any social science of economics, sociology, or psychology. In some remarks he anticipated a remark by Jayaprakash Narayan to the effect that if economics must be instructed about what it is to do, then it is a technology, not a science.

14. Quoted in D.G. Tendulkar, *Mahatma*, Volume II, pp. 212-23 and Vol. IV, p.34.

4

Aurobindo and the Quest for Superhuman Life

THE writing of Aurobindo Ghose stands as creative synthesis making sense of a remarkable career as a political activist, as a student of Indian tradition, and as a mystic and *yogin*. Having devoted fifteen years to an effort to destroy by any means British rule in India, he dropped the nationalist work even before Gandhi came on the scene and spent the next thirty-five years in near seclusion practicing *yoga* and writing books considered by many to carry principles necessary for human fulfilment in a technological society.

One of three boys born to a Bengali, English-educated physician, Aurobindo with his brothers was sent to England at the age of seven to receive what his father thought to be a proper education. Aurobindo remained in England until he age twenty-one, studying at St. Paul's under scholarship and later at King's College, Cambridge. He learned Greek, Latin, French, German, Italian, and Spanish and read widely in Western literature as prerequisite for a degree in Classics.

While at Cambridge Aurobindo became disenchanted with the sort of people who were preparing for careers in

the Indian Civil Service. He sat for the written exa-
minations and passed them, but he deliberately failed
the compulsory horsemanship examination. The
deliberate failure signalled a commitment to Indian
tradition.

Aurobindo returned to India in 1893 and was hired
in the service of a Maharaja of Western India to help in
the State Service of Baroda, a dominion retaining status
independent of the British Government of India.
Aurobindo taught French and English at Baroda College
and served for a time as vice-principal. He also took up
the study of Sanskrit and Bengali. And he began serious
study and practice of *yoga*.

But by 1904 Aurobindo was back in Bengal. A
British Intelligence report (dated 1904) claims that
since 1902 Aurobindo had been a ringleader of a
revolutionary group.

> He has ever since [1902] been the principal
> advisor of the revolutionary party, and
> has consulted about and in touch with
> their proceedings and crimes. He has
> been very careful, as far as possible to
> keep himself out of sight, and to prevent
> any trace of his presence or work being left
> behind. The result is that though we have
> valuable proof of his important share in
> this conspiracy, the legal evidence is not so
> strong. But it is of utmost importance to
> stop his power for michief; for he is the
> prime mover, and can easily get tools, one
> to replace another.[1]

Aurobindo served for a time as editor and writer for two
nationalist newspapers, *Jugantar* and *Bande Mataram*.

But in May of 1908, Aurobindo was arrested in connection with a bungled bombing in which the wrong people were killed ("the Maniktolla Bomb incident"). Confined to the Alipore Jail as an undertrial prisoner denied bail, Aurobindo practiced *yoga* and experienced what he later claimed to be realization of the "silent, spaceless and timeless Brahman". He found also the necessary means to silence forever a fellow prisoner capable (and willing) to give testimony against him.

One year after his arrest, Aurobindo was acquitted of charges against him on grounds of insufficient evidence. He re-joined the nationalist efforts by writing and editing two new journals, The *Karmayogin* and *Dharma*. But quite suddenly in 1910 Aurobindo withdrew from the freedom movement and travelled to Pondicherry, a French territory along the coast south of Madras. There for the rest of his life he practiced an intense *yoga* and wrote extensively in areas ranging from poetry to drama and from metaphysics to *yoga* practice.

Aurobindo the freedom-fighter and Aurobindo the metaphysician might seem incompatible. But a study of both his nationalist writings and his later work in philosophy suggests that he found sufficient justification for revolt to lie deep within Hindu tradition. Yet for Aurobindo national freedom was to be but a beginning for India. The country, he maintained, ought to take a leadership role in forging a new destiny for humanity. Indians, and indeed all of humanity, must evolve toward superhuman life.

Aurobindo the Freedom-Fighter

Aurobindo's involvement with nationalist revolutionaries in the early years of the twentieth century was

no mere burst of youthful enthusiasm. His commitment
to the freedom effort was grounded in a commitment to
Indian tradition. In a series of brilliant intellectual
moves Aurobindo drew from tradition justification for
revolt against British rule. Aurobindo laid out the case
for revolt in his *Bande Mataram* writings and in a
number of speeches. In short, his claim was that spiritual
freedom (*Moksha*) and political freedom (*swaraj*) were
so closely joined conceptually that political freedom
must be regarded as the necessary condition for any
realization of spiritual freedom. He wrote,

> It cannot be for a moment contended that
> we can again be spiritually great without
> being politically dominant. The Indian of
> today is not the noble, heroic, and self-
> sacrificing Indian of a bygone age, only
> because with the loss of political freedom
> his soul has also begun to pine and wither.
> Those who allow others to take possession
> of their body cannot long remain in
> possession of their soul. There cannot be
> a more mischievous delusion than to
> suppose that we can advance our soul by
> committing our bodies to the care of
> foreigners.[2]

And again,

> Swaraj [political freedom] is the direct
> revelation of God to this people — not
> mere political freedom, but a freedom vast
> and entire, freedom of the individual,
> freedom of the community, freedom of the
> nation, spiritual freedom, social freedom,
> political freedom. . . . Without political

freedom the soul of man is crippled. Social
freedom can only be born where the soul of
man is large, free, and generous, not
enslaved to petty aims and thoughts. . . .
Spiritual freedom can never be the lot of
many in a land of slaves. . . . When India
was free, thousands of men set their feet
on the stairs of heaven, but as the night
deepened and the sun of liberty withdrew,
the spiritual force inborn in every Indian
heart became weaker and weaker until
now it burns so faintly that aliens have
taken upon themselves the role of spiritual
teachers, and people chosen by God have
to sit at the feet of men from whose ancestry
the light was hidden. . . . By our political
freedom we shall once more recover our
spiritual freedom.[3]

Aurobindo identified political freedom as the necessary
condition for a realization of spiritual freedom. To his
mind political freedom (*swaraj*) was the sufficient
condition for freedom from British rule, and it was a
necessary condition for Indians to be Indians. As the
Hindu tradition had maintained for centuries, in order
to experience liberation (*moksha*) a person must be free
from attachments, from dependency, from any coercion
forcing a person to act in prescribed ways.

Yet a second move Aurobindo made was to show that
the various traditional systems of Hindu philosophy as
well as traditional expressions of devotion among Hindus
could provide sufficient motivation for nationalist efforts.
Political freedom was not simply in the best interests of
Indians materially (Indians might be 'better off' if they
ran their own economy). Political freedom, he main-

tained, was the proper condition for human beings (to be free is to be truly human). Tradition shows that, Aurobindo maintained.

Drawing upon the work of Vivekananda, a highly respected nineteenth-century exponent of Hindu thought, Aurobindo reiterated the claim that Hindu religious thought and modern science are not in conflict. Moreover, Aurobindo employed Vivekananda's expansive and inclusive interpretation of Hindu religion to show that the gods worshipped by many Hindu devotees are best understood as manifestations of the Absolute *Brahman* which is essentially impersonal and beyond human cognition. Aurobindo's gloss on Vivekananda added the significance of femininity to the activities motivated by *Brahman*.

> In the unending revolutions of the world, as the wheel of the Eternal turns mightily in its course, the Infinite Energy, which streams forth from the Eternal and sets the wheel to work looms up in the vision of man in various aspects and infinite forms. Sometimes She is Love, sometimes She is Knowledge, sometimes She is Renunciation, sometimes She is Pity. The Infinite Energy is Bhawani, She is also Durga, She is Kali, She is Radha the Beloved, She is Lakshmi, She is our Mother and Creatress of us all.[4]

Aurobindo identified this time to be the age of Shakti, 'energy'. But the energy at work in the world is in essence feminine, it is the energy of *Brahman* revealed in the world through creativity. It is the power of energy manifest as feminine that can bring about new life.

Let us raise our eyes and cast them upon the world around us. Wherever we turn our gaze, huge masses of strength rise before our vision, tremendous, swift and inexorable forces, gigantic figures of energy, terrible, sweeping columns of force. All is growing large and strong. The Shakti of war, the Shakti of wealth, the Shakti of science are tenfold more mighty and colossal, a thousandfold more prolific in resources, weapons and instruments than ever before recorded in history. Everywhere the Mother is at work; from her mighty and shaping hands enormous forms . . . are leaping forth into the arena of the world. But all of them are the Mother in her new phase, remoulding, creating. She is pouring Her spirit into the old; She is whirling into life the new.[5]

India as a country enslaved by British rule needs the strength of the Mother for regeneration. Devotion to the Mother, then, is central to India's freedom struggle.

We call her to come, but the call has not yet gone out from the bottom of our hearts. The Mother's feet are on the threshold, but she waits to hear the true cry that rushes out from the heart before she will enter. The Mother asks for all before she will give herself. . . . Those who aspire to free India will first have to pay the price which the Mother demands. Regeneration is literally re-birth, and rebirth comes not by intellect, not by the fullness of the purse, not by

policy, not by change of machinery, but by
the getting of a new heart, by throwing
away all that we were into the fire of
sacrifice and being reborn in the Mother.
Self-abandonment is the demand made
upon us.[6]

Aurobindo identified the goddess as the force of *Brahman*
at work in the freedom movement. But that force, he
claimed, was not confined to the freedom movement; it
was pushing and pulling in all areas of human creativity
— science, economics, art, indeed, religion.

Aurobindo's use of traditional symbols and ideas to
explain the Indian situation and to motivate revolutionary activity continued with his use of notions of
karmayoga and *sadhana*. *Karmayoga*, a teaching
advocated in the *Bhagavad-Gita* section of the
Mahabharata, is a discipline of self-mastery to the point
that any attachment or identification with the consequences of actions performed will not occur. Arjuna,
the Pandava fighter troubled by anticipated consequences of a clan war, listened to counsel provided by
his chariot driver, who happened to be Lord Krishna.
Krishna provided Arjuna a vision of time working
relentlessly, continuously, inevitably to swallow up
armies, people, wealth, glory. He saw all things of this
world to be subject to the rule of time. And Arjuna was
encouraged to understand that occurrences in the
material world are beyond the control of any human
being. All events are part of a great cosmic movement.
Thus, even to identify with consequences of a Divine
action is a mistake.

For Aurobindo the proper conclusion to be drawn
from the *Bhagavad-Gita* dialogue was that the struggle
for Indian freedom must be understood as part of a much

greater movement in time. A worker for freedom must
be a person willing to act in any manner necessary to
promote the movement. In short, a freedom-fighter
must be both free from attachments to consequences
and free to be and to do what is necessary for national
independence.

> The Aryan protects the friendly, smites
> the unfriendly. But he has no attachment.
> He sees the divine everywhere, in all
> beings, in all things, in all works, in all
> results. He has equal disposition towards
> good and evil, friend and foe, pleasure and
> pain, virtue and vice, success and failure
> .... He is not afraid of hurting. He does not
> hate his enemy, he is not unjustly partial
> to the friendly. For the sake of duty he can
> slay his own people, and save the
> opponents's life, giving up his own.[7]

Aurobindo recalled his prison experience:

> He [Krishna] placed the Gita in my hands.
> I was not only to understand intellectually,
> but to realize what Sri Krishna demanded
> of Arjuna and what he demands of those
> who aspire to do His work, to be free from
> repulsion and desire, to do work for Him
> without the demand for fruit, to renounce
> self-will and become a passive and faithful
> instrument in his hands, to have an equal
> heart for high and low, friend and opponent,
> success and failure, yet not to do his work
> negligently. I realized what the Hindu
> religion meant.[8]

Aurobindo insisted that what Indian needed for the freedom movement was a group who would fight the way Arjuna fought: without thought of reward, without caring about consequences, but to act with precision, skill, and dedication.

Sadhana is a term associated with the discipline of *yoga*. Traditionally the word connoted a person's personal means toward realization, which is to say, a private *yoga*. Such a discipline would be prescribed by a teacher (a *guru*). Aurobindo was convinced that since the movement for political freedom (*swaraj*) was linked to spiritual freedom (*moksha*), there must be a *yoga* appropriate to the task. Yet a selection of a *yoga* was governed by pragmatic criteria: a teacher prescribed what would work under particular conditions and for a particular practitioner. Freedom-fighters must adopt the same principle:

> The choice of a subject nation of the means it will use for vindicating its liberty is best determined by the conditions of its servitude.[9]

Given the conditions of India's slavery to the British, Aurobindo decided passive resistance to be the only feasible choice for direct action. Yet passive resistance, Aurobindo insisted was "the practice of freedom". Since, according to Hindu teaching, people are already free (they just do not realize their true condition), passive resistance would be to put into practice what is already the case.

The procedure of passive resistance was to be directed toward making laws unworkable through non-compliance with them. It would employ first boycott (buy no British goods, attend no government school, take no case to a government court, ignore all government agencies). And then the obvious corollary would be *swadeshi* ('one's own', and connoting 'home-made', or 'self-help'). Indians must make their own goods, establish their own schools, employ their own legal methods, and develop their own system of defence and protection.

Passive resistance as a *sadhana* would be a discipline. What it puts into practice is an expression of the innate freedom of the nation.

> Boycott is the practice of independence. It was no mere economical revolt we were instituting but the practice of national independence; for the attempt to be separate and self-sufficient economically must bring with it the attempt to be free in every other function of a nation's life.[10]

And again,

> Boycott is much more a mere economical device, it is a re-discovery of national self-respect, a declaration of national separateness; it is the first practical assertion of independence and has therefore in most of the national uprisings of modern times been the forerunner of the struggle for independence.[11]

Aurobindo and the Future Evolution of Human Life

Aurobindo insisted that his system of thought providing motivation for revolt was based upon the ideas stated by ancient sages of India. These thinkers maintained that behind the phenomenal world of sense experience there is a Conscious Power. They termed this Power *Brahman*. To emphasize the transcendent nature of this power, Aurobindo referred to it as *Paratparabrahman*, "*Brahman* beyond the beyond". The conscious power behind the phenomenal world of our experience is ultimately unknowable. But the universe is an expression of that power (this is to say that the power is ontologically prior to the universe, but in no way separate from it). Everything, from ships, shoes, and sealing wax to the most refined and subtle expressions of thought are extensions and expressions of *Brahman*, the One Power in which and through which all people think, and act, and have their being.

Moreover, all that exists, all that has being, are united in this one power in such a way that all are united in that one great self that is spirit. Aurobindo took from the Sanskrit Hindu tradition the three words *sat*, *cit*, and *ananda* to characterize the way in which the power expresses itself in the world.[12] All beings are united in the One Self, the essence of divine power from which all that exists emerges. But because of a separateness of consciousness that occurs through the involution process by which the One Self sends out the universe, ordinary people tend to be ignorant of their true nature. Ordinary people do not know that their true self, their true reality in mind, life, and body is a unity with the Ultimate Power of the universe. Aurobindo maintained that through certain traditional disciplines of *yoga* as he developed them, the veil of ignorance which creates the sense of separateness can be removed, and a person might realize the Divine power within.

It is important to remember that the One Power manifest in the world resides even in matter. Everything contains within it *sachchidananda*, everything contains 'existence', 'consciousness', and 'bliss'. *Sat* refers to existence, but existence as *sat* is ultimately beyond the human mind's capacity to comprehend. *Cit* is consciousness, it is the force of Being expressing itself as consciousness (Aurobindo maintained that every level of existence carries some measure of consciousness, even rocks and bottles and shoes). *Ananda* is absolute, eternal, unlimited bliss and delight. All of the universe is this Reality expressed through *sachchidananda*, through existence, consciousness, and bliss.

The process by which the One Power that is beyond the beyond, *Paratparabrahman*, expresses itself in the world is by a process of involution. Through involution the Divine consciousness manifests itself differently at various levels which Aurobindo was able to experience and to name as he progressed in his discipline of *yoga*. Every level of expression contains within it *sachchidananda*, which is to say that the Divine is 'folded' into the world as creation proceeds down a scale which ends only with the emergence of matter. In the final expression of *sachchidananda* in matter only existence is apparent, but technically consciousness and bliss must be somehow there also.

The first expression of *sachchidananda* is what Aurobindo termed Supermind. Prior to Supermind, of course, there exists *sachchidananda* unmanifest and unknowable, the Ultimate Power of the Universe. But a second level below Supermind occurs in which particularization takes place as the Ultimate Power chooses that individual, conscious beings emerge. These beings bring about or permit the development of individual personalities on levels still to emerge. Then Overmind emerges out of Supermind, and from Overmind emerges Mind, the level where human life appears. Mind, however, has different levels, too: there is the Intuitive Mind, which carries an awareness of Overmind; there is the Illumined Mind, which is a consciousness independent of conceptual thought; and there is Higher Mind, which carries a sense of the divine unity, but it engages itself with thinking and reflecting.

Below the Higher Mind is the level of ordinary human cognition, the level of Mind. Humanity in general exists on the level of Mind. It is limited, it is characterized by ignorance because it tends to restrict itself to its particularizing capacity (it is the level of scientific and technological activity), and it fails to comprehend the divine unity of the very force from which it emerges. It often appears to be bewitched by analysis, particularity, precision, efficiency, and organization.

Below the level of Mind are the levels of Soul (or Psyche), Life, and Matter. A Soul retains a sense of unity with the divine, but until it becomes aware of unity with the Ultimate Power it is inclined to identify with Matter. Life is the force in plants and animals which raises them above the level of dirt and rocks. Matter is the furthest expression of Divine Consciousness. But Matter is also *Brahman*, and thus it must carry some minute dimension of consciousness. Matter is most bound to what science identifies as Natural Law, particularly the Laws of Space, Time, and Causality. But Matter is also the culmination of a movement toward particularity. Matter seems incapable of Unity; so it is at the same time the endpoint of Involution and the beginning of evolution back toward *sachchidananda*.

The whole of the universe, therefore, is in a process of evolution whereby the Divine is returning to itself from what appears to be an unconsciousness of Matter to the Supermind and finally to *Sachchidananda*. Because the whole world is being drawn toward the Divine, what is happening in Nature is Nature fulfilling itself (it cannot be seen as nature destroying itself). The scientific theory of biological evolution misses the important issue of involution, and therefore scientists are able to find no clear meaning or significance to the process. But if the process begins with the descent of God into matter, then meaning and significance to evolution appear.

A most important characteristic of the evolutionary movement is its integrality. The lower rises into the higher, but the lower does not cease to exist. The lower is pulled higher and infused and modified by the higher. Matter evolves to produce life. But matter does not cease to exist. Nor does life cease with the appearance of mind, of intelligence. All becomes integrated at a new level.

Today human intelligence is changing the material world by every new technology that is developed. Human beings are not what they were one hundred years ago. Nor is nature what it used to be. But what is moral and right and good in such a conception of reality is whatever promotes development toward divine perfection. The process of evolution at the level of Mind allows (indeed, requires) a conscious participation by people. Human beings can and ought to participate in the return toward Supermind. The disciplines of Aurobindo's *Yoga* assist in this movement of ascent toward new life.

On the other hand, evil does exist. Evil consists of those acts which hinder the evolutionary process. Aurobindo maintained that it is possible for a society to repress and to standardize life to the extent that the divine force is repressed and/or diverted. Efforts to repress the force are those efforts that push conformity, compliance, custom, and even false piety. Efforts to divert the Divine impulse are those which try to re-direct the force toward ends which do not contribute to growth, progress, or development. Evil in this sense might spring from fear, from pride, from a compulsion to preserve and to retain what is inapplicable and inappropriate to a new time and a new age.

But evil is not absolute. Its beginning lies in ignorance, a failure (sometimes a willing failure) to comprehend the divine unity toward which all is moving. Particular instances of evil, then, might be regarded as educational. Pain, suffering, sickness all indicate that a person has stepped in a direction contrary to the evolutionary process. The occurrence of such evils should serve as a reminder to live in conformity to the process of return toward the Divine.

Aurobindo's claim, then, is that Divinity as One Being and Consciousness is involved at every level of reality, ever Matter. Involution is a process by which Divinity releases itself and extends itself to create matter. Then consciousness appears out of Matter and it is impelled by the force of *Brahman* to develop toward greater and greater spiritual unity. Mind has evolved. It is the level at which most people live today. But there is no reason to assume that Mind as it is expressed today is the end of the development. Aurobindo claimed that his mystical experiences confirmed the Overmind and the Supermind as levels of consciousness above the life of Mind.

Humanity needs to move beyond the level of mind. But such a move will not occur by mental effort alone. The move beyond must be done through the psychological disciplines of *yoga*. In the past such disciplines drew people away from the world. But Aurobindo insisted that because the whole of the world is the involution and evolution of *Brahman* as *sachchidananda*, a descent of the higher principle of Supermind is possible which will release divine power into the world, transform it, and draw it higher.

The world is waiting for humanity to be transformed into a Super-human race. In other words, humanity as humanity is today but transitional, not final. Neither is the mind of today the highest possible level of consciousness. Nor is human life the highest possible form of life in the world. "The step from man to superman is the next approaching achievement in the earth's evolution".[13]

Mystical Conclusions and Cognitive Issues

Aurobindo did not wish to have his views confused with ordinary philosophy. Any appeal for verification of his assertions could only be found through religious experiences. He grounded his ideas by appeal to *shruti* texts (as most Hindu teachers might do), but he did not consider conformity with Hindu scripture to be verification for his ideas. Nor did he appeal to logic or to science for verification. Instead, 'true intuition' gained through the practice of *yoga* were grounds for certainty.

Nevertheless, Aurobindo's writings carry empirical claims that follow from experience. Teachings about levels of consciousness, teachings about the nature of *sachchidananda*, teachings about the real existence of Overmind and Supermind, indeed, the whole spiritual worldview asserted by Aurobindo constitute claims of an empiric nature. Aurobindo recognized that he was a 'mystic empiricist', one who was making truth claims concerning the reality of the world as well as the peculiar unity of *Brahman* with the phenomenal world.

A major question for Aurobindo's readers, of course, is whether mystical experience is objectively informative. Does mystical experience provide information about the object world (or does mystical experience convey information only about the workings of an individual mind).

The question is further complicated if the 'objective' claims of two or more mystics disagree or even contradict one another. It is the case that Aurobindo in an early period of *yoga* practice experienced "the silent, spaceless and timeless Brahman . . . attended . . . by an overwhelming feeling and perception of the total unreality of the world".[14] But such an experience was later sublated by further experiences which convinced him of the reality of the world. Because Aurobindo himself had experiences which superseded prior experiences and convinced him that reality was other than what he had thought earlier, might it be the case that some mystic could have an experience which supercedes Aurobindo's spiritual worldview? Any experience, it seems, which sublates ordinary sense experience and shows it to be inferior might itself be sublates. And this process might go on forever. How might a person know that he or she has had the final experience? And if it cannot be known that a person has had the final experience, what sense (or truth) are we to give to what a person says about any experience? One experience of Aurobindo's convinced him that the world was unreal. Later experiences convinced him that it was real.

Yet further conceptual difficulties arise from Aurobindo's spiritual worldview that begs for an explanation of the meaning of both Freedom and

Determinism. A general problem of Freedom and Determinism arises for ordinary people whenever they become aware of an apparent conflict between beliefs based on two different sets of facts. On the one hand, there are obvious facts which convince people that they are responsible morally for their behavior and that it is correct that praise or blame be given for what they do. But whenever praise or blame are assigned to someone, the assumption behind the assignment is that the person was free to do otherwise. That is to say, human freedom is assumed with every moral judgment made.

Yet, on the other hand, another set of facts (which today seem almost self-evident) convince people that every event in the universe is an inevitable consequence of some antecedent causes (every event, it seems, has a cause). This conviction is the assumption behind all scientific inquiry and explanation (events are governed by laws of order which can be stated with mathematical precision: "pure water freezes at 32 degrees Fahrenheit at sea-level barometric pressure.") This is the Deterministic view: every occurrence is the consequence of prior causes.

The intellectual problem is posed by the question of whether Freedom that is a condition for moral responsibility can possibly be the case if Determinism assumed (and verified) by science is the case. Is the Freedom that is a condition of moral responsibility compatible with the Determinism that is observed in all of Nature?

Aurobindo in discussing this problem employed Vivekananda's expansive and inclusive cosmology which allowed him to affirm science at the same time as he affirmed Hindu tradition. When discussing evolution, Aurobindo employed a traditional Hindu view of causal

relations known as *satkaryavada*, namely that an effect
in the material world emerges out of a cause (in short,
there is an essential identity between a cause and its
effect). The view is held by such traditional systems of
Hindu thought as *Sankhya*, *Advaita*, *Dvaita*, and
Vishishtadvaita. Such a view of the causal process
observed in the world serves to confirm the conviction
that because the universe is an expression of *Brahman*,
the essence of all that is created is Divine. But such a
view is compatible also with the Determinism assumed
by science. But is there reason to hold people morally
responsible for their acts if Determinism is the case?

Aurobindo slips past the issue of conflict by asserting
that human beings are both determined and free, they
have been produced as they are by a causal process, but
they are free to choose (and thus they are responsible for
their choices).

> If we go back to the true Hindu teaching
> independent of Buddhist influence we shall
> find that it gives us a reconciliation of the
> dispute by a view of man's psychology in
> which both Fate and Free-will are
> recognized.[15]

Aurobindo appealed to the Sanskrit word *Dharma* as
correlative to the notion of scientific Determinism: "It is
that by which the action of the universe, the action of its
parts, the action of the individual, is held together".[16]
Karma is the application of this universal law to human
experience. People are the result of previous actions, the
principle of *karma* maintains, and these actions might
be traced back through habits, tendencies, and
inclinations which determine the choices people make.
But, Hindu teaching has been insisting for centuries.

That these determining conditions are the very things from which a person needs liberation. That is to say that if there is only this law of Determinism (*karma*), then life is a bondage and there is no hope for freedom.

> There can be no escape, unless there is something within us which is free and lord, superior to Nature. This entity the Hindu teaching finds in the spirit ever free and blissful which is one in essence and in reality with the Supreme Soul of the Universe.[17]

Freedom is known in the spiritual life of a person. Freedom is a realization achieved by a person having spiritual experience. Only the spiritually realized person is free. And that person is aware of a life above and unattached to the determinative laws that govern the material world.

But one must ask if this is a solution to the problem as it has been traditionally structured in the West. Instead of addressing the moral problem of Determinism, Aurobindo sublates that problem to a spiritual issue. Human beings are a duality. Residing within each person is a free, inactive, observing spirit above the laws of space, time, and causality. The traditional structuring of the problem of Freedom and Determinism fails to recognize that human life, which might be seen ordinarily to be hemmed in by Determinism, is being drawn to a higher level of spiritual realization where people might act appropriately through a supramental awareness of the ways things are. The traditional structuring of the problem by Western thinkers is inappropriate to the reality of the human situation, according to Aurobindo.

An issue related to the problem of Freedom and Determinism is the cultural issue of technological determinism. In short, the question put is whether or not, in the process of divine evolution, the force of technological commitments (technological culture) allows freedom of choice about technology's advance. Or are people being driven to live according to the dictates of technology. A troubling issue for some is the sense that technological culture seems to gradually erode selfhood as it has been thought about for years. Traditional notions about individualism, of personal autonomy, rights to privacy, rights to self-determination and self-realization all seem threatened by the commitment of nations and states to increasing levels of technological organization. It seems that machine technologies, electric technologies, and the electronic 'information' technologies force a new way of life upon people. And all of these reduce the sphere of the individual and eliminate many former means for self-realization and fulfillment. Technology seems to be the major determining factor about how people are going live in the contemporary world.

Aurobindo's ideas concerning technology are tied consistently to his notion of a divinely ordered process of evolution. What is occurring in the contemporary world is but a stage in human development. Evolutionary development began prior to human life. And there is no good reason think that development should end with human life as it is known in this particular time. People today are the consequence of a driving force toward greater and greater complexity as the divine spirit pulls itself back toward *Paratparabrahman*, "the ultimate power beyond the beyond". Development, evolution, is determined, it is a progress, it is inevitable, and it requires new ways of thinking, new social organizations, and an abandonment of obsolete ways of thinking about people and things. The intellectual baggage carried by important Western philosophers of the eighteenth century might have no relevance to this time. Even as Aristotle or Plato would not have the slightest idea of how to live with and manage the technologies of today, neither would such thinkers as Locke, Rousseau, Hobbes, or Kant. All has changed; and it is wise for people to scrap ideas and values which are incompatible with the necessary changes that are occurring.

References

1. Confidential Note, May 19, 1908, Minto Papers, Correspondence, Vol, I.

2. *Bande Mataram*, 2 August 1907.

3. *Ibid.*, 23 February 1908.

4. *Bhawani Mandir* in *Bande Mataram, Early Political Writings,* Sri Aurobindo. Pondicherry: Sri Aurobindo Ashram, 1973.

5. *Ibid.*, pp.61-62.

6. *Bande Mataram*, 13 April 1908.

7. "National Resurgence", In *Sri Aurobindo Mandir Annual,* No. 27 (1968), p. 20. This is an article appearing initially in Dharma, 1909-10, and translated by the Sri Aurobindo Ashram.

8. "Uttarpara Speech", In *Sri Aurobindo Speeches* (Pondicherry: Sri Aurobindo Ashram Trust, 1969), p. 49.

9. "The Doctrine of Passive Resistance", In*Bande Mataram*, p. 97.

10. *Bande Mataram* 6 August 1907.

11. *Ibid.*, 14 August 1907.

12. The three words are put together to form one descriptive

term according to various methods of transliterating Sanskrit into an English alphabet. Aurobindo's transliteration is *sachchidananda*.

13. *The Hour of God* quoted in Sisirkumar Mitra, *Sri Aurobindo*, New Delhi: Indian Book Company, 1972, p. 196.

14. Quoted in Sisirkumar Mitra, *Sri Aurobindo*, New Delhi: Indian Book Company, 1972.

15. "Fate and Free-Will", In *Man — Salve or Free?* Pondicherry: Sri Aurobindo Ashram, 1966, p. 25.

16. *Ibid.*

17. *Ibid.*, p.27.

5

Jayaprakash Narayan and Gandhian Reconstruction

IN March of 1977 a remarkable event occurred when a coalition of groups opposed to the thirty-year rule of the Congress Party pulled off an election coup at the Lok Sabha elections. Calling themselves the Janata Party, this disparate group of opposition parties, won a startling and decisive victory after but a few weeks of campaigning.

Defeat for the Congress Party was a matter of great concern not only to those who lose in the election but to those who study Indian history and culture. Many observers from the West concluded that the heave-handed use of modern technological procedures by Congress leadership to deal with India's social and economic sectors were important factors in a people's revolt. At the top of the list of complaints were slum clearances in major urban areas and an aggressive program of mass sterilization.

To delay and to discourage public and political opposition, Prime Minister Indira Gandhi had declared a government and social Emergency to exist on 26 June 1975. Acting on powers ceded by the Constitution to the President, Mrs. Gandhi ordered the arrest of hundreds

—even thousands—of people thought to be endangering her program of modernization. In all, over 110,000 people were jailed in the 21 months of the Emergency. Constitutional Rights were suspended, arrested people received no particulars of the charges against them, newspapers were forbidden to publish names of those arrested, and Parliament acted to delete retroactively from the Constitution crimes charged against Mrs. Gandhi and the Congress leadership.

It was thought by many that the alleged 'excesses' of the Emergency moved voters to rally to the Janata coalition. But another factor in the success of the coalition was the leadership role played by Jayaprakash Narayan. Although 'JP' had never held political office and had renounced Indian political activity in the early 1950s, he had appeared again as someone for the politicians to contend with in 1974. An enigma to many observers who rely upon traditional categories of analysis and appraisal, JP had travelled many roads, from Marxism to Socialism to Vinoba Bhave's *Sarvodaya* and *Bhoodan* ideals.

The *Manifesto* of the Janata coalition was a puzzle for many political analysts. Most had assumed beforehand that the text would be a jumble reflecting the disparate interests of the coalition parties. But instead, a text reflecting consistent Gandhian social and political principles appeared—principles that the *Times of India* labelled 'Neo-Gandhism'. The major ideas, it was contended, could be traced to Marxism, Leninism, and Maoism, together with a profound disillusionment with the industrial technology of America and Western Europe. The *Times* labelled it "a new variant of ritualism for which India and Indians have been well-known".[1]

The ideas of Jayaprakash Narayan dominate the

text of the *Manifesto*. The text indicates that what India was facing was a critical situation generated by the problem of how to put into practice modern democratic and technological values at the same time as the traditions of India were maintained. The *manifesto* stated, however, that the Janata coalition was committed to the values and ideals of Mahatma Gandhi. These include, it stated, a recognition that a high degree of centralization and concentration of power are actually inconsistent with the ideals of democracy. And public officials are to be examples of simplicity and selfless service, not experts in public relations and propaganda.

Priorities of government must be given to raising living standards of the poorest sections of society, the *Manifesto* stated. A decentralization of industries and expanded support for cottage industries should take place. Moreover, primacy must be given to agricultural and rural development, not urban industrial development. A minimum wage must be established to protect all working people, and individual 'self-reliance' must be promoted by government procedures. At the same time the *Manifesto* insisted that the Janata was pledged to "preserve the secular and richly diverse character of our state".[2]

The personal involvement of Jayaprakash Narayan in the opposition movement provided two important elements for the coalition. First, he gave the Janata a broad ideology which could combine Constitutional values of justice, liberty, equality, and fraternity with spiritual ideals espoused by many who identified themselves with the Hindu majority in India. Second, he was known for his commitment to the welfare of rural India because of his association with the Gandhian program for the rural sectors called *Sarvodaya*, "the uplift of all".

The blending of these factors (a broad ideological base along with an appeal to villagers), together, no doubt with the moral significance of the fact the JP had been imprisoned during the Emergency, elicited support from both urban and rural sectors.[3]

Yet one might argue that JP's ideas were consistent with the social values of the Indian Constitution (in spite of his imprisonment by the congress Government as a subversive). To secure "to all citizens, **justice**, social economic and political; **liberty** of thought, expression, belief, faith and worship; **equality** of status and of opportunity; and to promote among them all **fraternity**" had long been personal goals for JP. From the time of his return to India in 1929 (after studying at The University of California, the University of Iowa, the University of Wisconsin, and Ohio State University), he had drifted from Marxist thought to Socialist thought to *sarvodaya*. But his changes of mind had been only changes with regard to how best the ideals of justice, liberty, and equality might be realized in India at the same time as appropriate technological development might occur.

Although Narayan had joined Congress efforts to oust the British from India, he was never comfortable with the Congress Party. He viewed its post-Independence leadership to be too prone to compromise and too content with less than total realization of the values of justice, liberty, and equality. Until the achievement of Independence, JP had been a Marxist, insisting that his interpretation of Marx was the correct one, even though the India Communist Party and the Socialist Party disappointed him. And by 1953 JP was ready to confess, "Both Socialism and Communism are faced with failures".[4]

JP insisted that in Russia, Communism must lead

inevitably to state capitalism; in Europe, Socialism must lead inevitably to parliamentary politics based on compromises and deals among bureaucrats. Talk of justice and equality would be done only to secure votes. In the end, people would be abandoned and forgotten by the politicians.

Moreover, he insisted, a socialist state could not produce the goods for India either. Even if the government managed to achieve goals of ending hunger and poverty, that would not be enough. And the reason it would not be enough, he claimed, was that such measures would not address the fundamental problems of dislocation and strain produced by the new social situation required to implement the government plans for large industrial development. A nation of well-fed and clothed brutes was to his mind not all that the Constitutional statements implied.

JP concluded that if the government pursued plans for major industrial development and high technology solutions to India's economic development, popular initiative, activity, and commitment would disappear. Individual fulfillment as expressed in Constitutional values would not and could not be achieved through large-scale industrial development. In JP's view, it was wrong for India to adopt the culture of technology as it was being pushed by politicians at the top levels of government.

A solution JP proposed was to return to the principles of Mahatma Gandhi. Although politicians since Independence had used the name of Gandhi with embarrassing regularity to sanction policies that ranged from free enterprise to socialism, they were merely doing what politicians are prone to do. Even the Congress Party talked of Gandhi from its position of supremacy at the same time as it ignored the needs of the countryside and committed itself to urban industrial development. Talk of Gandhi by Congress politicians "is just a concession", he maintained.

JP's solution to India's situation assumed two principles. First, that the loss of individuality required by Socialist efforts of technological development were intolerable. And second, that only a moral assent by the people of India to any program for development could make a modern, prosperous, secular government function effectively.

Yet the rhetoric of the Jana Sangh and the RSS calling for a return to 'Hindu' culture did not appeal to JP. Gandhian teaching concerning *Sarvodaya*, however, did promise a means for social reconstruction at the same time as it recognized that individual human beings possess a desire for human fulfillment. "Social reconstruction is impossible without human reconstruction", he wrote. The promise of *Sarvodaya* is that it gives first a moral base for social action; then it provides a technique for achieving the proper goals of social action; and finally it advocates a program of decentralization as a way to preserve individual dignity, aspirations, and a moral order.

It was in 1954 that JP underwent a conversion experience of some sort. He participated with others in a *Jeevandan* ceremony — a public dedication to the social and moral ideals of Gandhi. Yet he maintained that such a commitment was primarily one of adopting a new strategy for achieving the old goals.[5] The proper method to be used to re-shape society in harmony with constitutional requirements and traditional goals was the *bhoodan* movement being developed by Vinoba Bhave at that time. *Bhoodan*, JP insisted, could lay a groundwork for change, a change which would be both a return to traditional values and a recognition of the realities of a technological culture. But to lay such a groundwork, he said, "Conversion must precede legislation".[6]

Bhoodan as a movement encouraged landowners to give land gifts (*bhoodan*) to landless peasants. The plan was to convince landowners to give up what was theirs for the good of other people. What was fundamental importance to the act of land-giving was that it required a change of heart and mind, a creation of a new sense of social responsibility, a new sense of relationship to other people. Narayan wrote:

> Not heart or mind has been changed by law; no individual made virtuous by coercion. *Bhoodan* is thus a great mass movement of conversion and the creation of a new climate of thought and values in life. It brings about a living and immediate revolution in the minds of men and their mutual relationships. What *bhoodan* says about land... is true of all our possessions, including even knowledge and skill.[7]

The land gift, JP thought, would be but the beginning of 'total revolution', a requirement for India to successfully integrate tradition with modern technology. Giving land is the easiest place to start in the transformation of individuals, he believed. Land itself is a gift of nature; it belongs to all. Land was there before any individual person was born, and it will be there after any individual person dies. Moreover, land is a relatively easy thing to give up , since all people have equal claim to earth and no one can long argue a special claim to it. And once the

act of a land gift is made, a new way of thinking, a new
conception of human relations, a new sense of identity
with a whole culture will begin to dawn upon people.

Such a re-making of individuals is a first step in a
larger task. But construction of a new social order
demands first the construction of a new type of human
being. The *bhoodan* method shifts attention from political
activity toward a reconstruction of individual and moral
values and attitudes. Only moral people can create a
moral society.

> I would like to define a socialist society as
> one in which the individual is prepared
> **voluntarily** to subordinate his own interest
> to the larger interest of society.[8]

JP cited historical precedent for the land gift. The
agents of land gifts in the past were village elders who
divided land according to their view of who deserved
land.

> In the divine dispensation land rightly
> belongs to him who works on it. This is
> also in keeping with our ancient cultural
> traditions. In ancient times land belonged
> to the village community, and the village
> *panchayat* distributed the same to the
> village people every twenty or twenty-five
> years, in accordance with the number of
> members in a family. This was dictated by
> the principle that nobody should have
> more land than he needed.[9]

In short, JP claimed, the land gift is a return to traditional
cultural values; but more, it is a step toward ending
greed — and greed, he insisted, is a value encouraged by

the culture of technology. But rather than start by building an organization for political action, *bhoodan* immediately puts into practice the values of the society which all people might wish to enjoy. The Gandhian principle that means and ends must coincide is affirmed — a principle running counter to the values of technology, values which recognize only means but can decide upon no end.

Convincing arguments for the moral values upon which a new society might rest need not be imported to India from outside its own traditions, JP maintained. A moral base for a just society is to be found within India itself. In delineating a moral base, JP relied heavily upon a vocabulary that has widespread appeal to a large segment of urban, educated, white-collar Hindu Indians.[10]

JP relied heavily upon Vivekananda's interpretation of Indian tradition as a way to point out a moral base for re-making society. Vivekananda's interpretation of Indian tradition as he delivered it to Western audiences in Europe and America provided expansive boundaries for Indian thought by asserting that Darwin's theory of evolution was but a gloss on ancient Hindu theories of the emergence of the world, that the First Law of Motion confirms the Hindu goal of *Moksha*, and that the original purpose of *varnaashrama-dharma* was the establishment of a society more democratic than any based upon European thought. The frame-work provided by Vivekananda maintained that Indian tradition testifies to a Golden Age of antiquity, an intellectual heritage that dwarfs traditional Western systems of speculative thought, and a political system that carries a unified, consistent, and remarkably democratic theory of social and political order relevant to the modern world.[11]

To reconstruct Indian society JP appealed to the model society suggested by the Orientalist theory of India's Golden Age. A moral base upon which to build a just and free society today, he held, can be found within the traditions stemming from the ancient India. And he cited both the *varna* system and the function of *dharma* within that society he was convinced existed sometime in Indian antiquity. "India was perhaps the earliest home of democracy", he maintained in an article titled "Reconstruction of Indian Polity". The early polity, he insisted, may have used kingship as a mode of rule; but kings were elected by and subject to the *kshatriya* aristocracy.[12]

Some village communities managed to maintain the tradition, and they managed to hold together a stable and efficient polity of democracy not only through various kingdoms and dynastic changes, but even into the British period of rule. The traditional community order expressed itself in two forms. The first and most basic form was the village or township. The second was the functional or occupational community, the *varna*. People who performed the same functions and who held similar occupations in society had common rights and responsibilities. The *varna* system eventually declined into a system of institutionalized discrimination known today as the caste system. But the two fundamental truths of the early *varna* system persist and are relevant to the modern situation. Human beings do have different aptitudes and abilities; they should be free to pursue and develop those aptitudes and abilities. And these two truths from antiquity form a moral base for democracy. Each person deserves an opportunity to develop his or her inherent abilities. And society must be structured to provide for that.

The flaw in the Western democratic theory is that it is based upon a notion of 'natural rights'. Constitutions of many Western nations maintain that citizens have certain rights which the government must recognize and protect. Among theses are rights to life, liberty and the pursuit of happiness. The flaw is that any democratic system built upon a notion of rights will force each individual to act against other individuals in order to realize personally and individually those rights. Internecine warfare, aggression, competition are built into and remain a necessary part of the structure of the Western democratic creed.

The ancient system of *varnaashrama*, however, divorced from the later accretions of heredity and privilege, held that each individual is born with tendencies and abilities that will lead that person into a certain occupation or vocation. The ancient system allowed people the freedom to pursue an inclination toward the intellectual life, the managerial life, the mercantile life, or the life of service to society.[13]

Another factor in the early democratic order of India was the concept of *dharma*. Regulations for individual and group behaviour stemmed from *dharma*. But also the regulations for communities and groups across village and even state boundaries were a part of *dharma*. Codes and laws common to everyone made up a social ethic which regulated life for ancient Indians.[14]

Democratic order in India was destroyed by alien governments which entered with the deliberate purpose of imposing a new order upon India. The roots of *dharma*, therefore, no longer are much in evidence in India. Commerce, education, labour, administration and the priesthood have no regulation that Indians can share as a community of people. And because *dharma* used to be intimately associated with the communal lives of people, the removal of it from Indian life has been a disaster.

To transplant European principles and laws will not be a substitute. Laws and regulations based upon traditions that differ from the traditions of India will not work. In fact, the new laws, so far as they have been adopted in India, have put village against village, class against class, city against city, and state against state in order to gain advantages and power for a privileged few. But the ancient concept of *dharma* can be revived and translated into terms fit for a modern society so that India can realize the ideals of freedom, equality, and liberty along with non-violence, respect for law, and tolerance.

Western modes of democratic polity implanted by the British and adopted by the framers of the Indian Constitution actually imply a negation of the social nature of mankind as expressed in traditional Indian culture. Western principles assume that society is made of an inorganic mass of separate grains of individuals. They assume that the individual is an autonomous, unhindered, unhampered person without constraints of culture society or family. Moreover the system of the West transforms the individual into a vote and then into a statistic to be grouped with other statistics. Power is distributed according to the massing of arithmetical sums. The Western political systems begin by assuming that the individual is autonomous and end by eliminating that autonomy by turning the individual into a number.

But the defect from which all other problems of Western political order issue is that the Western democracies operate on the false premiss that a state can be constructed from the sum of individual votes. Yet people cannot be reduced to statistics. And to attempt to operate a country upon such a premiss is to allow for the situation that prevails in many countries where a political party might reach power without even achieving a majority of the votes cast in an election. And even then, the winner represents not the people who voted but forces and interests providing money and propaganda for a party to win votes. The need to attract votes creates an unlimited opportunity to indulge in half-truths and to arouse base passions of people.[15] To think that it is really democracy that prevails in the United States or any European country is to make a serious mistake in judgment.

Yet another problem with "democracy as it is practiced in the West is the tendency toward centralism. The creation of bureaucracies at the centre of governments puts a focus upon party interests over the interests of individual citizens. A bureaucracy controls the power and resources that really belong to the people. But the system itself reduces individual citizens to insignificance. The so-called sovereign citizens are not allowed to decide how much power the state is to exert over their affairs. And, often what the bureaucrats do with the power they are given is to shuffle it among large interest groups of bankers, industrialists, and trade unions to see who might provide the greatest advantage to the bureaucracy of the state, not to the people. In the process, the parties themselves become a state within a state, run by groups of politicians that are beyond the control of the voters.

The faults of centralization, however, might be avoided for India by a return to the ancient village system of democracy. The old system would invert the bureaucratic pyramid of power. Goals that people are concerned to achieve would be set by people at the level of the village. And the means to achieve those goals (i.e., technologies which they would determine to be 'appropriate' to their village) would be established.

For JP, the first level of organization in a democratic society must be the village, the primary community of Indian people. Adults of a village could meet regularly as members of a general assembly (*gram sabha*) to decide how to solve common problems and to establish goals for their community work. A selection of some villagers to serve on a village council (*gram panchayat*) would take place by a drawing of lots (an ancient village procedure). There need be no parties, no candidates, no campaigns. Those selected would have the task of seeing that no one in the village went without food, clothing or shelter: that all children had access to education; that all received primary medical care; and that everyone could work so that a minimum standard of living might be achieved. The values of the Constitution would not be denied. But local people would decide how to realize for themselves a self-sufficient community.

A next level of organization, would soon be necessary. A regional group representing each village council would be formed by villages selecting a representative to a regional council (*panchayat samiti*). The work of the regional council would be to integrate the institutions, activities, and concerns of the primary communities. In turn, the regional council would select representatives to district councils (*zillaparishads*). District councils could form a provincial community, and provincial councils might federate to form a national community.

According to JP, the outer communities or councils should have fewer matters to attend to than the village councils. The national community could handle matters of defence, foreign relations, currency, and inter-provincial co-ordination and legislation. All activities at both village and national levels would be under the check of shared moral law and a traditional social ethic.

The ethic espoused at the community level would be, quite naturally, the welfare of all within it. But the planning to realize such welfare must begin with local people. Any regional or national concerns about planning for the welfare of communities would be merely procedural, not legal or executive.

The primary economic activity of a village would be agriculture. Each village would require only enough industry to provide for fundamental needs of local people. All technology would be appropriate to the requirements of the local economy. In short, justification for industry would be the supply of local needs, not profit. Should one village in a provincial area need equipment or goods that only another village in the provincial area can produce, the village councils and regional councils would arrange proper trading channels.

The organic relation between primary villages and towns might continue to grow. But economic decentralization, small-machine and labour intensive industry, together with a partyless democracy would pave the way for a non-violent, new society for India, a society free from the exploitation endemic to large-scale industry, free from the destructive competition generated by capitalist industry, and free to value brotherhood and equality.[16]

Decentralization would also return moral values to their proper sphere, the minds and wills of individuals. Concentration of power into bureaucracies tends to remove individuals from either an ability to make moral decisions or from a sense of responsibility about decisions they see themselves forced to make. Large institutions (from corporations to social welfare agencies) make decisions that discount or eliminate the significance of personal moral codes or rules. That is to say that large institutions **force** decisions of a particular sort upon both the people who serve the institutions and the people served by the institutions. And once an individual senses that in a state system he is either morally helpless or morally unaccountable, the great values of freedom, justice, and equality are lost.

Gandhism and Tradition

What is achieved by combining Constitutional values with traditional cultural values is a synthesis of normally disparate ideals. Socialism, with its aim of economic improvement as a key to human fulfillment, ordinarily must be seen as counter to traditional Hindu aims of individual liberation (*moksha*). The aims of Marxist and non-Marxist forms of Socialism to improve human life by creating a society in which economic prosperity and security are the possession of all seem contrary to traditional Hindu goals of personal liberation from such concerns. Moreover, the Socialist aim requires a restructuring of society. Elimination of poverty comes by a distribution of material resources according to needs rather than according to social position or inherited wealth. And human fulfillment is thought to come by the creation of a society that promises welfare to all.

The thrust of traditional Hindu thought, on the other hand, directs people toward a contemplation and a realization of an individualistic goal.[17] The human predicament, according to *shruti* and *smriti* texts, is one of bondage to *karma* and *samsara*, not poverty, exploitation, injustice, and inequality. The goal is liberation from the wheel of existence (*samsara*) that is controlled by the inexorable law that a determinate consequence follows from every human act (*karma*). Social rituals and rules are to be found in the sacred literature. But the texts subsume the claims of social life to the ultimate goal of liberation. Day-to-day life in a society is to be controlled by the rules which prepare a person for an eventual move beyond society.

JP's views were found compelling to many because he was able to unite what may at first appear to be disparate goals. He shows that *sarvodaya* and *bhoodan* coalesce both with the Constitutional values of justice, equality, liberty, and fraternity and with the moral values contained in Indian tradition. For JP, it is possible for a person to declare allegiance to the Constitution at the same time as a person holds to significant teachings from ancient Hindu texts.

JP wrote little of *moksha*, however. And when he did, it was to interpret the concept in such a way as to eliminate any incompatibility between the tradition and the Constitution. He chose to see *moksha* as part of a broad social frame-work that ordered the society of ancient India.

> The Indian ideal life is expressed by the four concepts: *artha, dharma, kama, moksha*. As everyone knows, they designate the wholeness of life. *Artha*: we must win our bread; *kama*: we must seek pleasure and achieve it.... all this pursuit of *artha* and *kama* must be within the context of social responsibility [*dharma*].[18]

According to JP, *moksha* is in one sense a move beyond the other three concerns. But it is also a consummation of the concerns being expressed in the other three. *Moksha* finally transcends the temporal concerns of mankind. But the way toward *moksha* is learned through the integration of *artha* concerns, *kama* concerns, and *dharma* concerns. And even if the final goal of *moksha* results in a move beyond the social life, Indian tradition allowed for it by ordering previous concerns.

The fundamental insight, however, is that the ideal social order expressed in Indian tradition is compatible with the socio-political values of the Constitution, which are in turn values which many think to be required for life in democratic and industrial societies. Moreover, Indian tradition makes it possible to pursue a spiritual goal at the same time as necessary social, political, and economic concerns are affirmed. For JP, the social values of Indian tradition and values of the life committed to democracy and technology are the same. Moreover, the tradition suggests how best to realize those goals in an Indian society.

Mrs. Gandhi's Emergency declaration and the draconian procedures used to enforce it threatened the abolition of those ends toward which JP had directed his life. In his own words, his life had been a striving to secure "freedom of man everywhere and from every sort of trammel — above all . . . freedom of the human personality, freedom of the mind, freedom of the spirit. This freedom has become a passion of life and I shall not see it compromised for bread, for power, for security, for prosperity, for the glory of the State or for anything else".[19]

The elections of 1977 that rejected Mrs. Gandhi and her Congress program for large-scale industrial development and population control measures seemed to indicate that JP's message mattered to a lot of people in India. But JP's ideas were never put into place. Instead, India saw a new group of politicians setting about to do what politicians everywhere do: amass power to enjoy power. And soon after the new government entered, Jayaprakash Narayan died. One must wonder if he was as disappointed as Mahatma Gandhi.

References

1. *Times of India*, 29 June 1977.

2. "Text of the Janata Manifesto", In The *Times of India*, 10 February 1977. A remarkably similar statement appeared under JP's name in *Everyman's* of 1 December 1974 and appears again in his book titled *Towards Total Revolution*, Vol. 4, pp.110-14.

3. JP's arrest was to many Indians a symbol of the vindictiveness of Congress politicians: he had never held public office, he had restricted his activities to work developing village technologies, and was, at the time, an old and sick man.

4. His disillusionment with Society Russia came early. By 1939, he said, ". . . we discovered that the Communist Party of Russia . . . was prepared to compromise its ideals for the sake of Russian nationalism, while the Communist Party of India was advised to sacrifice India's national interests for the national interests of Soviet Russia." The occasion was Stalin's pact with Hitler, and then the Nazi invasion of Russia. See the essay "New Doctrine", In *Toward Total Revolution*, Vol. 2, p. 216.

5. 'Jeevandan", in *Socialism, Sarvodaya and Democracy*. p. 123.

6. *Ibid.*, p. 134.

7. *Ibid.*, p. 124.

8. *Ibid.*, p. 134.

9. A source for such a precedent is not cited by JP.

10. A. Bharati and others have referred to this vocabulary
    in a pejorative sense as 'Neo-Hinduism'. What seemed
    to trouble Bharati was what he thought to be an
    unsophisticated appreciation of Indian tradition which
    identifies 'Hinduism' with something somewhat different
    from what one might find by consulting an actual
    historical text. Bharati's point is that religious
    sentiments expressed by many of those people who run
    India from her urban centres, while they might claim to
    stem from authentic Indian sources, are unspecific
    enough to be virtually unconnected to any traditional
    school of Indian religious-philosophical thought.
    Moreover, Bharati claimed that the sentiments would
    be for the most part unfamiliar to villagers of India. See
    "The Language of Modern Hinduism", In *Religious
    Ferment in Asia*, ed. by Robert J. Miller and "Hare
    Krishna Vs. Shiva Siva", *The Illustrated Weekly of
    India*, March 17, 1974, p. 32.

11. By *tradition* I mean those ideas important to the present
    which might be used to re-tell the past in a way that
    suits current conditions or demands. Tradition might
    be given in a literal fashion or it may be changed as
    current conditions demand that it be changed. A
    historian, on the other hand, is required to remain
    uncontaminated by the demands for a re-statement or
    re-telling of the past. That JP does not to my knowledge
    engage in serious research about the complexities of
    Indian history and/or schools of thought and that he
    sometimes appealed to texts normally classified *as smriti
    as though they were shruti*, suggest to me that JP was
    engaged in what was for him a necessary revision or re-
    statement of the past. But, indeed, by my own definition
    of tradition, he was doing what cultural theorists do.

12. There is an early Buddhist text suggesting that as part
    of cosmic decay, *varna* distinctions arose, private
    property and family became institutions, and crimes
    multiplied. All of these produced the need for the

selection of one man to maintain order, and so one was selected by the people. On the other hand, texts such as *Manu* (VIII. 3-5, 8), *Ramayana* (II. 57), and *Mahabharata* (XII. 67) support the idea of royal divinity. And *Aitareya Brahmana* (I. 14) and *Taittiriya Upanishad* (I. 5) tell the story that because gods and demons were at war it was required that a king be appointed. Indra was duly appointed. Any claims to divinity by kings of India may follow from these sources. In all cases, however, the function of a king was to protect social order (*varnaashrama-dharma*). See A.L. Basham, *The Wonder That Was India* (Chapter IV) and J. Duncan Derret in "Social and Political Thought and Institutions", In *A Cultural History of India*.

13. The scheme is derived from Vivekananda, whose statements appear in *The Yogas and Other Works* and they are reiterated by Radhakrishnan in *The Hindu View of Life*, pp. 76-81.

14. "Reconstruction of Indian Polity", in *Socialism, Sarvodaya and Democracy*, p. 206. The theory is further developed in "Building up From the Village", a talk on All India Radio, April 1959, printed in *Towards Total Revolution*, Vol. 3, p. 85, and in "How to Cut Deadwood in Administration", in *Everyman's*, August 24, 1973.

15. "Reconstruction", p. 214.

16. *Ibid.*, The system JP describes was not unknown to South India, according to Burton Stein in "Integration of the Agrarian System of South India", In *Land Control and Social Structure in Indian History*, ed. by Robert E. Frykenberg, pp. 179-88.

17. See Joan V. Bondurant and Margeret Fisher, "The Concept of Social Change in Hindu, Socialist, and Neo-Gandhian Thought", In *South Asian Politics and Religion*, ed. by Donald Eugene Smith, pp. 235-48.

18. "Building the National Community", In *Three Basic Problems of Free India*, p. 23.

19. Jayaprakash Narayan, *The Evolution Towards Sarvodaya*, p. 5.

6

India's Future in the Culture of Technology

WHAT of India's future in a world where technology is a main measure of achievement? Must India pattern itself after America or Europe to solve problems both internal and external? Might India possess resources from her tradition to provide a pattern for technological development unique to the Indian situation? Or must everyone everywhere learn to live the way Americans or Europeans live to enjoy what modern technology might bring?

The crucial question, of course, is whether or not India's tradition might have any relevance to the new order imposed by technological innovation. Can Indian tradition contribute to rapid and comprehensive technological development? Or might ideas and values from India's past hold her back from the technological development her leaders seem to think she needs? Is it possible to continue to hold to ways of the past at the same time as modern technological devices are adopted?

It is the case that technology rarely confronts or counters traditions directly. So the culture of technology often does not appear to be a threat to a tradition. But technology erodes traditions, reducing their significance in a number of ways: by suggesting new meanings to the symbols and stories passed along; by implying that values of the past are irrelevant to the present order of things; and by forcing social changes which render former ways of life unstable.

Thinkers such as Mohandas K. Gandhi and Jayaprakash Narayan maintained that India could employ technology in ways consistent with traditional India. But such technology would not be the technology of the West. Gandhi fashioned a plan both for rural and for urban development which he thought to be consistent with traditional ways. His plan never received official support, however, even though for years it has been difficult to find a successful politician who has not wanted to identify with 'Gandhism'.

It is a fact that Indian leadership after Gandhi thought that his ideas would constitute a step backward. To let technological innovation begin with the concerns and interests of people living in India's villages, to recognize self-help and self-reliance as basic requirements for improved social conditions, to design production technologies for the masses (not the other way around) seemed simplistic to independent India's leaders.

Jayaprakash Narayan re-asserted Gandhian principles twenty years after Gandhi's death. He received considerable attention and respect. And a coalition of politicians and parties opposing the Congress Party programs managed to win office in 1977. But the Gandhian principles were never really put into practice. In short, India does not know if Gandhi's ideas might actually work.

Sri Aurobindo, on the other hand, treated technology as one of a number of abstract issues characteristic of one level of evolutionary development. In our time, technology is a product of the level of Mind in which attention is given to analysis and particularization. As analysis and particularization, technology manages to produce new and mighty creations. These creations possess the capability of drawing people toward a recognition of the Divine unity that is the ground of all being and meaning. But an inappropriate fascination and identification with technology might divert people from the strong pull toward unity. Aurobindo taught that all particulars emerge out of *Brahman* and are grounded in *Brahman*. A proper orientation to the culture of technology requires the attention and advice of people properly enlightened through the practice of *yoga*.

Government leaders since independence, however, have put little confidence in the teachings of Gandhi or Aurobindo. Instead, leaders have been convinced that India might best advance in the world by adopting a Western model of government and social development. A democratic political structure was thought to promise India a secure place of respect among those nations espousing human rights. Prosperity and power, it was thought, were sure to follow if India adopted Western ways in economics, communications, and education. Under the leadership of the Congress Party beginning in the 1950s and extending with but minor interruptions into the 1990s, a primary effort was made to develop large-scale capital-intensive urban industries utilizing labour-saving technologies. The pattern for development came directly from the West. And because the villages of India produce no major goods for foreign trade, generate little investment capital, and place small value upon progress, village life, in fact, was regarded as something of an obstacle to progress. This despite the fact that eighty per cent of India's population live in the villages.

Some people today suspect that many of the serious problems that India now faces follow from the Western model of development that India took. The list of problems is extensive. Nuclear technologies (India was quick to develop them) Promising to make people more safe and secure have instead made life unsafe and insecure for Indians. Nuclear weapons let India join the nuclear explosion club, but they also put India into dangerously tense relations with her neighbours and with nations of the West. Nuclear reactors to generate electrical power for the benefit of India's millions discharge dangerous contaminants which accumulate in the air and water. Large-scale industrial technologies severely degrade natural environments by destroying the previous balance of ecosystems and by pollution. The increased risks to human life and to social and natural environments which seem to invariably accompany large-scale industrial development remain a constant problem to India's urban landscapes (the Bhopal disaster was an extreme instance of what many think might be happening daily on a smaller scale where industries give little attention to pollution control measures). Moreover, the major cities of India are covered by blankets of smog making any form of physical exertion — even breathing — sometimes difficult.

Human health is threatened in more subtle ways by the chemical technologies. New pesticides designed to control insects and weeds on the farms, additives to make food commercially appealing, and waste disposal systems that pollute air, soil, and water all take a toll on the health of Indian people. The infectious diseases which plagued India in the past now are joined by the new killers that mark the Western nations: heart disease, stroke, and cancer. Mental illnesses ranging from severe depression to schizophrenia to psychosis contribute to increasing social disintegration characterized by violent crime, suicide, and alcoholism. And India continues to live with an increasingly uneven distribution of income and wealth.

This unhappy situation forces India now to face the questions that haunt the so-called developed societies of the West. All of the questions are related to questions about Technological Determinism. Is it the case that the troubles and problems characteristic of modern, affluent societies follow from a tendency of technology to erode those values which might preserve a traditional order? Is the price of sophisticated technology the loss of those values which formerly held together diverse societies? Is modern technology the disease for which it has been intended as cure?

The experience of India suggest that Technological Determinism is the case. Modern technology has forced changes upon India. But how extensive is such forced change? And what control might people have over the change?

One answer is pessimistic one: technology is a force which slowly but pervasively erodes and destroys traditional ways. This I have labelled the Hard Determinist view. It is the view that India will inevitably become like Western nations in every way because once modern technology enters it takes control and completely drives a society. The symbols, stories, ideas and values of Indian tradition will fade only to reappear as tools in the service of the new culture of technology. Moreover, a Hard Determinist will insist, there are no alternatives once modern technology enters a society. People must give into it or die as a people and as a society.

A second response is that of the Soft Determinist. These thinkers insist that modern technology provides only the occasion for the problems mentioned. Forces that bring about such problems lie deeper than technology. A Soft Determinist argues that it is Western culture that is the cause for the problems characteristic of technological societies. India need not fall prey to the problems if India recovers its distinct ways.

But, Indian leaders in their eagerness for development, mistakenly adopted some of the pre-suppositions of Western societies. Four of those presuppositions are crucial for the sort of troubles introduced to India along with technologies which have seemed so important to development. The first of these is the presupposition that human beings are autonomous individuals possessing rights and freedoms which a society is required to protect. This presupposition was spelled out in America as early as the Declaration of Independence: "We hold these truths to be self-evident, that all men are created equal, that they are endowed by their Creator with certain unalienable Rights, that among these are Life, Liberty, and the pursuit of Happiness". This as a presupposition about what is basic to a good and proper life tends to run counter to any conviction that responsibilities to village or caste or family are more important than personal fulfillment. Such thinking has put ambition, competition, and even aggressive acquisitiveness, at the core of social life.

A second important presupposition is that time is linear (not cyclical) and that progress continues to take place as history proceeds (the world is better today than it was one hundred years ago, we assume). This, too, is a presupposition running counter to any notion that a proper pattern for life in the world was established in the past, and that life is best lived according to the values of the forefathers. Not all people everywhere equated progress with technology.

Yet a third presupposition is that to use the resources of nature will make for a better life. Nature exists for human beings to exploit as they see fit, is the view. Because people are superior to nature, they possess a right to do with it what they might wish to do. This as a presupposition holds that might makes right (because it can be done, it is right to do it).

And fourth is the presupposition that wealth and consumption are the major indicators of a successful life in the world. A good life, it is thought, is a life of abundance and the enjoyment of the comforts which abundance might bring.

It is not a difficult matter trace the present problems of an unequal distribution of wealth, inordinate exploitation of natural resources, and a disregard for the past (for history and tradition) to such presuppositions. More difficult is the matter of what to do about these problems should they be seen as directly linked to technological development. Can sophisticated development occur without presupposing what Western societies presuppose? Might India solve through technological innovation her serious economic problems without endorsement of deleterious Western presuppositions?

India in the past held to significantly different ideas from those of the modern West. A main function of government, it was presupposed, was to strengthen a sense of duty and responsibility to the ruling authority (the rights and freedoms of individuals are of secondary concern). Moreover, Indians were taught by the great teachers of the past that abundance and the consumption it encourages might stand in the way of real human fulfillment by encouraging **grasping**, a far less significant value than **giving**. Time, Indian thinkers note, is continuous, but not necessarily progressive. Innovation and change that occur might be threats to the principles of proper order established in an earlier age. Goodness is a characteristic mark of the past, and to maintain the old ways with regard to family and society are basic to morality. And what marks reality is a unity which at its deepest level is undivided. Particular differences observed are simply expressions of the underlying unity, which is what is really real. These are traditional Indian ideas.[1]

But is it possible to adopt modern technology and still hold to such presuppositions? Reports from India in popular media suggest that Indian leaders are having to re-discover and to think again about traditional ways in order to deal effectively and consistently with the new technologies imported from the West. For example, in the large corporations patterned after corporations of the West, it is discovered that business principles of the West do not work very well in India. Competition among employees, which it was assumed would follow from beliefs about autonomy and individualism, does not occur among Indians. Indians prefer to find ways to work together. They prefer a work environment where a sense of community and cooperation prevails. So new terms and new management strategies to fit the Indian mind—terms and strategies which appeal to 'integrative cooperation' and 'shared vision' instead of competition — are being developed in some of India's major corporations. In short, it seems that traditional values make a difference for how a modern Indian business functions. Sometimes those traditional attitudes even frustrate the efficient operation of a business. But managers are encouraged to incorporate the traditional values into their management plans.

Ruben Banerjee, a writer for *India Today*, a *Time magazine* clone, has note that Indian workers struggle with concepts imported from the West, but respond well to images and themes drawn from traditional symbols and stories. One explanation for such a preference for traditional symbols and stories is that a 'collective unconscious' is being tapped when symbols and stories from the past are re-told. Banerjee notes that many companies are having some success resolving difficulties of employee misgivings about requirements of industrial work through seminars for workers that explain to them the contemporary significance of the great books of India. The tradition speaks to workers, is the claim. One lecturer notes, "The *Vedas* combine the dynamism of the West with the peace and serenity of the East". And another insists that the *Bhagavad-Gita* fits with requirements posed for Indians by the culture of technology: "It is about self-management", he said.[2] These suggest that a creative re-thinking of traditional texts can be done as a response to the culture of technology.

Yet the culture of technology forces adjustments to traditional ways. A significant area of adjustment is with marriage and family relations. The joint family pattern of India's past does not fare well with the modern values of individualism, equality, and personal freedom. The traditional Indian joint family—patrilineal in descent, patrilocal in residence, and patriarchal in authority— never tolerated individualism and personal freedom over commitments to family unity. The extended family was always a single unit. The living patriarch was the chief source of authority in all matters. Each member of a family had a carefully defined set of responsibilities. And personal matters ranging from daily duties to marriage were decided not by an individual but by the elders of the family. High value was placed upon conformity.

But today a joint family living in an Indian city faces new realities. In the first place, a family itself is eliminated as a producing agent within society. In the countryside, a family might function as a producer of most goods necessary for survival. And it serves also as the prime socialization agent for children. But the culture of technology breaks apart the traditional family by separating work from residence and by encouraging economic diversification within the family. The men of a joint family household might have to find work in places a considerable distance from the family residence. Separation from residence creates a number of complications. Major time is spent away from the extended family members, there are many contacts with strangers, and an increasing number of possible interpersonal relations develop. Acquiring skills necessary for employment requires a readjustment of a person's identity as a family member who works to provide a living wage. Moreover, industrial work, which is often piecemeal work done in a factory, creates a whole new set of psychological problems for workers that can range from alienation to depression and boredom.

Economic diversification extends into the household where work-reducing appliances allow at least some women of a family to seek employment, recreation, or community service projects outside the home. A woman finds it necessary to redefine a role as wife and/or mother: a working women in many ways frees herself from complete economic dependence upon a man and this requires that some aspects of a marriage relationship must be re-defined. In an urban setting, it is possible for a woman to find some significance to her life apart from the home. Children of a family attend schools which are concerned to teach them not about the past but about how they might successfully enter the technological society.

An additional factor which complicates the family situation is the technology of contraceptives. Because contraceptives separate sex from reproduction, the family itself system becomes just one of a number of ways to order sexual relations. Contraceptive technologies, then, force an adjustment in thinking and living. If a family is no longer the primary agent ordering sexual relations within a society (if sex and reproduction are separated in the minds of people), a family itself becomes less important than it used to be.

Yet studies of families of India suggest that the traditional pattern continues with only minor adjustments. Changes do occur. Yet it is still possible to find many urban households with twenty or more people living together. The price of real estate, the low wages paid for many jobs, and the high cost of living in India's cities make a joint family arrangement a convenient option.

But changes from strict autocratic hierarchical structure where the word of the patriarch was law is taking place. A new joint family structure is beginning to appear. The new joint family is more of a federation held together by compromise and convenience. To have a mother-in-law within the same house to watch children if a wife pursues a career is a convenience not to be ignored by an ambitious woman. And a wife finds that to compromise about many matters which might

otherwise disrupt a household is fairly easy when support
in her role as a working woman occurs on a regular basis.
Moreover, the paycheck brought home by a wife to help
defray household expenses or to purchase a few luxuries
has a way of smoothing over what might otherwise be
irritating intrusions by a mother-in-law. In short, the
old joint family is giving way to a new joint family
arrangement (one might even say that the traditional
family is getting pulled through the knothole created by
the culture of technology). Problems still arise: How
necessary is a common kitchen? Whose domain is the
kitchen? Who is to see to it that household chores are
done in a proper manner? But such questions seem
ubiquitous to families.

What seems to be emerging in India is a new family
structure that is characteristic of the companionship
family that is praised but rarely practiced in America.
Held together less by patriarchal authority or rigid rules
than by mutual affection, division of labour, and
respectful communication, the new family structure is
an adaptation to the realities of life where the culture of
technology invades a traditional society. The difference
with India is that it seems to work.

In these two ways — in business practice and in
family relations — tradition continues to make a big
difference for the people of India in spite of the changes
forced by the culture of technology. But these are only
two areas of adjustment. Larger issues of environmental
decay which follow from technological innovation remain.
It seems obvious that India will not do well by following
the path mapped by the wealthy nations of the West. To
squander fossil fuels, to dump wastes whenever and
wherever they might be dumped, to pollute indis-
criminately soil, water, and air in the name of develop-

ment will be a grave error. Yet India's remains with a problem it had fifty years age: poverty complicated by overpopulation.

But it might be the case that in these areas, too, India tradition provides a unique way to resolve issues of natural resource depletion, overpopulation, and poverty. Such a suggestion seems strange, because India is notorious for its problems in all of these areas. Yet attention to Indian tradition may provide practical solution to these problems.

Indian tradition reinforces modes of behaviour appropriate to what today would be termed a 'steady-state' society rather than a 'growth' society. A steady-state society is one in which there is no increase either in the number of people or in resource consumption. Such a society has never existed, but India may have the resources to create it — resources located in her long sense that duty is more important than personal freedom, that getting is not as important as giving, and that reality at its deepest level is undivided.

A steady state society would require many changes in the ways in which people live. The ratio of people to resource consumption would need to be rationally controlled to meet both reproduction requirements and limits to reproduction. At the same time controls would have to be established on resource consumption. This is to say that birth control would be co-ordinated by government planners so that a ratio of births to consumption would occur. Does India's long tradition of authoritarian government make such draconian measures feasible?

Further requirements for a steady-state would be put strict controls upon both economic development and resource consumption. To do so, the value of frugality would be made a primary value for the whole society (over against Western propaganda about abundance and consumption). Specific technologies to recycle materials for use over and over again would receive special attention. Labour intensive technologies (rather than labour-saving, energy-intensive technologies) would be developed. Renewable energy technologies (such as solar power) would receive increased attention. And curricula in schools and colleges would shift from applied science and technology toward the study of art, music, literature.

There are many today who think that such a new society is a requirement for the human race to survive. Nations of the West which base themselves upon a tradition of individualism and human rights to abundance and consumption appear to be doomed. India may carry the necessary traditional values to make a steady-state society a reality.

References

1. John M. Koller in his book *The Indian Way* (Macmillan, 1982) and Fritjof Capra in his book *The Turning Point: Science, Society, and the Rising Culture* (Simon and Schuster, 1982) lay out the significance of presuppositions guiding modern technology over against traditional presuppositions guiding modern technology over against traditional presuppositions of cultures East and West. I have relied a great deal upon their work in what follows.

2. *India Today* (July 15, 1994).

Bibliography

Adas, Michael. *Machines as the Measure of Men. Science, Technology, and Ideologies of Western Dominance.* Ithaca, NY: Cornell University Press, 1989.

Anderson, R. G. W. "Science and Technology in Indian Culture — a Historical Perspective", In *Technology and Culture* 27 (1986): p.p. 857-59.

Bhatt, V. V. "Development Problem, Strategy, and Technology Choice: Sarvodaya and Socialist Approaches in India", In *Economic Development and Cultural Change* 31 (1982): pp.85-89.

Bolle, Kees W. *The Persistence of Religion: An Essay on Tantrism and Sri Aurobindo's Philosophy.* Leiden: E.J. Brill, 1965.

Brown, Judith M. Modern India. *The Origins of an Asian Democracy.* Oxford: Oxford University Press, 1985.

Bruteau, Beatrice. *Worthy is the World: The Hindu Philosophy of Sri Aurobindo.* Rutherford, NJ: Fairleigh Dickinson University Press, 1972.

Capra, Fritjof. *The Turning Point, Science, Society, and the Rising Culture.* New York: Simon & Schuster, 1982.

Das, Manoj. *Sri Aurobindo.* New Delhi: Sahitya Akademi, 1972.

Ellul, Jacques. *The Technological Society.* Translated from the French by John Wilkinson. New York: Alfred A. Knopf, 1964.

————, *The Technological System.* Translated from the French by Jaochim Neugroschel. New York: Continuum Publishing Corporation, 1980.

Embree, Ainslie T. *Charles Grant and British Rule in India.* New York: Columbia University Press, 1962.

The Essential Aurobindo. Robert A, McDermott, ed. New York: Schocken Books, 1973.

Feibleman, James K. *Technology and Reality.* The Hague: Martinus Nijhoff Publishers, 1982.

Feys, Jan. *The Yogi and the Mystic: A Study in the Spirituality of Sri Aurobindo and Teilhard de Chardin.* Calcutta: Firma K L Mukhopadhyay, 1977.

————, *Sri Aurobindo's Treatment of Hindu Myth.* Calcutta: Firma K L Mukhopadhyay, 1977.

Fisher, Louis. *The Life of Mahatma Gandhi.* New York: Harper & Brothers, 1952.

Gandhi, M.K. *An Autobiography. The Story of My Experiments with Truth.* Mahadev Desai, translator. Boston: Beacon Press, 1956.

————, *Basic Education.* Ahmedabad: Navajivan Press, 1951.

————, *The Collected Works of Mahatma Gandhi.* 72 Volumes. New Delhi: The Publications Division, Government of India, 1958-78.

Ghose, Aurobindo. *The Future Evolution of Man: The Divine Life Upon Earth.* P.B. Hilaire, ed. Pondicherry: Sri Aurobindo Ashram, 1971.

———, *The Doctrine of Passive Resistance.* Calcutta: Arya, 1948.

———, *Speeches.* Calcutta: Arya, 1948.

———, *Man-Slave or Free?* Pondicherry: Sri Aurobindo Ashram, 1966.

———, *Sri Aurobindo Birth Centenary Library.* 30 Volumes, Pondicherry: Sri Aurobindo Ashram, 1970-76.

———, *Bande Mataram. Early Political Writings.* Pondicherry: Sri Aurobindo Ashram, 1973.

Heehs, Peter. *Sri Aurobindo: A Brief Biography.* Oxford: Oxford University Press, 1989.

Hutchins, Francis G. *The Illusion of Permanence. British Imperialism in India.* Princeton, NJ: Princeton University Press, 1967.

The Integral Philosophy of Sri Aurobindo: A commemorative Symposium Haridas Chaudhuri and Frederich Spiegelberg, ed. London: Allen & Unwin, 1960.

Iyengar, K.R. Srinivasa. *Sri Aurobindo. A Biography and a History* (2 Volumes). Pondicherry: Sri Aurobindo Ashram Trust, 1972 (First published: 1945).

Jayaprakash Narayan. *Towards Total Revolution.* (4 Volumes). Bombay: Popular Prakashan, 1978.

———, *Socialism, Sarvodaya, and Democracy.* Bimla Prasad, ed. New York: Asia Publishing House, 1964.

Johnson, David L. *The Religious Roots of Indian Nationalism.* Calcutta: Firma KL Mukhopadhyay, 1974.

———, Edward Pytlik, and Donald P. Lauda. *Technology, Change, and Society.* Worcester, MA: Davis Publications, 1978.

———, *A Reasoned Look at Asian Religions.* Minneapolis, MN: Bethany House Publications, 1985.

Juergensmeyer, Mark. "The Gandhi Revival—A Review Article", In *The Journal of Asian Studies* 43 (1984): pp. 293-98.

Koller, John M. *The Indian Way.* New York: Macmillan Publishing Company, 1982.

Leiss, William. *The Domination of Nature.* New York: George Braziller, 1972.

———, *Under Technology's Thumb.* Montreal: McGill-Queen's University Press, 1990.

McDermott, Robert A. "Philosophy and Evolution of Consciousness", In *Cross Currents* 39 (1989): pp. 322-38.

McGinn, Robert E. *Science, Technology, and Society.* Englewood Cliffs, NJ: Prentice-Hall, 1991.

Macaulay, Thomas Babington. *Macaulay, Prose and Poetry.* G.M. Young, ed. Cambridge, MS: Harvard University Press, 1952.

———, *Lord Macaulay's Legislative Minutes.* C.D. Dharkar, ed. London: Oxford University Press, 1946.

Michael, Loren. "The Indian Response to European Technology and Culture". In *Technology and Culture* 25 (1984): pp. 111-13.

Mills, James. *History of British India.* (10 Volumes). H.
Wilson, ed. London: J. Madden, 5th edition, 1858.

Minor, Robert. *Sri Aurobindo. The Perfect and the Good.*
Columbia, MO: South Asia Books, 1978.

Minto, Mary C. *India, Minto and Morley.* 1905-10.
London: Macmillan, 1934.

Mitra, Sisirkumar. *Sri Aurobindo.* New Delhi: Indian
Book Co., 1972.

Nehru, Jawaharlal. *Toward Freedom, the Autobiography of Jawaharlal Nehru.* Boston, MA: Beacon
Press, 1972.

Naik, J. P. "Development and Gandhian Tradition in
Indian", In *The Review of Politics* 45 (July 1983):
pp. 345-65.

O'Connor, June. *The Quest for Political and Spiritual
Liberation: A Study in the Thought of Sri
Aurobindo Ghose.* Rutherford, NJ: Fairleigh
Dickinson University Press, 1977.

Phillips, Stephen H. "Aurobindo's Concept of
Supermind", In *International Philosophical
Quarterly* 25 (1985); pp. 403-18.

———, "The Central Argument of Aurobindo's The Life
Divine", In *Philosophy East and West* 35 (1985),
pp. 271-84.

Prasad, Bimal. *Gandhi, Nehru and JP.* Delhi: Chanakya
Publications, 1985.

Postman, Neil. Technopoly. *The Surrender of Culture to
Technology.* New York: Alfred A. Knopf, 1992.

Potter, Karl. *Presuppositions of India's Philosophies.*
Englewood Cliffs, NJ: Prentice-Hall, 1972.

Purani, A.B. *Evening Talks with Sri Aurobindo.* Pondicherry: Sri Aurobindo Ashram Trust, 1970.

Radharkishnan. *The Hindu View of Life.* The Upton lectures R MNXHWARWE College, Oxford, 1926. New York: the Macmillan Company, no date.

Rudolph, Lloyd. "Cultural Policy in India", In *Pacific Affairs* 56 (1983): pp. 232-87.

Scarfe, Allen and Wendy. *J.P. His biography.* New Delhi: Orient Longman, 1975.

Shils, Edward. *The Intellectual Between Tradition and Modernity: the Indian Situation.* The Hague: Mouton, 1960.

Shinn, Larry D. "Auroville: Visionary Images and Social Consequences in a South Indian Utopian Community", In *Religious Studies* 20 (1984): pp. 239-53.

Smith, Donald Eugene. *South Asian Politics and Religion.* Donald Eugene Smith, ed. Princeton, NJ: Princeton University Press, 1966.

Sorensen, Georg, "Utopianism in Peace Research: The Gandhian Heritage", In *Journal of Peace Research* 29 (1992): pp. 135-44.

Stern, Robert W. Changing India. *Bourgeois Revolution on the Subcontinent.* Cambridge: Cambridge University Press, 1993.

Stokes, Eriic. *The English Utilitarians and India.* Oxford: Clarendon Press, 1959.

Teilhard de Chardin, Pierre. *The Divine Milieu: An Essay on the Interior Life.* New York: Harper & Row, 1965.

Tendulkar, Dinanath G. *Mahatma: Life of Mohandas*

Karamchand Gandhi, (8 Volumes). Delhi: Publications Division, Government of India, Revised edition, 1960-63.

Washbrook, David. "South Asia, the World System, and World Capitalism", In *The Journal of Asian Studies* 49 (1990): pp. 479-508.

Westrum, Ron. "Technologies and Society", In *The Shaping of People and Things*. Belmont, CA: Wadsworth Publishing Company, 1991.

Williams, George M. *The Quest for Meaning of Swami Vivekananda, Chico*. CA: New Horizons Press, 1974.

Winner, Langdon. *Autonomous Technology. Technics out of Control as a Theme in Political Thought*. Cambridge, MA: MIT Press, 1977.

Zaehner, Robert Charles. *Evolution in Religion: A Study in Sri Aurobindo and Pierre Teilhard de Chardin*. Oxford: Clarendon Press, 1971.

Index